MANAGING THE ENVIRONMENT
THE ROLE OF ECONOMIC INSTRUMENTS

ORGANISATION FOR ECONOMIC CO-OPERATION AND DEVELOPMENT

ORGANISATION FOR ECONOMIC CO-OPERATION AND DEVELOPMENT

Pursuant to Article 1 of the Convention signed in Paris on 14th December 1960, and which came into force on 30th September 1961, the Organisation for Economic Co-operation and Development (OECD) shall promote policies designed:

— to achieve the highest sustainable economic growth and employment and a rising standard of living in Member countries, while maintaining financial stability, and thus to contribute to the development of the world economy;

— to contribute to sound economic expansion in Member as well as non-member countries in the process of economic development; and

— to contribute to the expansion of world trade on a multilateral, non-discriminatory basis in accordance with international obligations.

The original Member countries of the OECD are Austria, Belgium, Canada, Denmark, France, Germany, Greece, Iceland, Ireland, Italy, Luxembourg, the Netherlands, Norway, Portugal, Spain, Sweden, Switzerland, Turkey, the United Kingdom and the United States. The following countries became Members subsequently through accession at the dates indicated hereafter: Japan (28th April 1964), Finland (28th January 1969), Australia (7th June 1971), New Zealand (29th May 1973) and Mexico (18th May 1994). The Commission of the European Communities takes part in the work of the OECD (Article 13 of the OECD Convention).

FOREWORD

Since the publication in 1989 of the first OECD survey and assessment of the use of economic instruments for environmental protection in OECD countries, the situation has evolved considerably. Not only has a greater number and variety of economic instruments been introduced in OECD countries, but their scope of application has also broadened to transfrontier and global environmental issues. Non member countries in transition to a market economy are also contemplating or are already in the process of applying economic instruments. In January 1991, the OECD Council adopted a "Recommendation on the use of economic instruments in environmental policy" requesting, that OECD review the actions taken by Member countries for a more consistent and wider use of economic instruments. In this context, the OECD Group on Economic and Policy Integration, carried out a new assessment of the situation in OECD countries and in European economies in transition.

This report presents the results of this survey. It has been prepared by Prof. **J.B. Opschoor** (Free University of Amsterdam); Dr **A.F. de Savornin Lohman** (Institute for Environmental Studies, Free University of Amsterdam); Dr. **H.B. Vos** (DHV Consultants) and the Secretariat. It is published under the responsibility of the Secretary-General.

Also Available

Environmental Policy: How to apply Economic Instruments (OECD, 1991)

Taxation and the Environment: Complementary Policies (OECD, 1993)

International Economic Instruments and Climate Change (OECD, 1993)

TABLE OF CONTENTS

Part I: Economic and Policy Background

Part II: Economic Instruments in Practice

Part III: International Aspects

Part IV: Conclusions and Prospects

PART I

ECONOMIC AND POLICY BACKGROUND

Chapter 1

Economic Instruments in Environmental Policy

1.1 The OECD project on economic instruments and its background

1.1.1 OECD position on economic instruments

The OECD Environment Committee at a Ministerial level meeting on the 30th and 31st January 1991, recommended that OECD nations should pursue a strategy in which integrating economic and environmental decision-making was the first of three elements [OECD (1991c), par. 15]. Elaborating on this, the Environment Committee proposed a number of principles to guide action by OECD governments, including the use of economic instruments, in conjunction with regulation, as an important tool for achieving policy integration [OECD (1991c), par. 16]. The OECD environment ministers considered economic instruments to be capable of providing strong incentives for technological innovation and behavioural change, and to offer good prospects for achieving environmental objectives in a cost-effective manner [OECD (1991c), par. 20].

The OECD Council subsequently adopted a Recommendation on economic instruments (C(90)177/final) which proposed *inter alia*:

-- a greater and more consistent use of economic instruments;
-- to improve the allocation and efficient use of natural and environmental resources by means of economic instruments to better reflect the social costs of using these resources; and
-- to seek further agreement at international level on using economic instruments with respect to solving regional or global problems and to ensuring sustainable development.

The history of the OECD position on economic instruments will be described below, after first introducing the project that the present report has emanated from.

1.1.2 The OECD 1992/1993 project on economic instruments

The Council Recommendation quoted above also instructed the Environment Committee to review the actions taken by Member countries pursuant to the Recommendation within three years.

The present report on the use of economic instruments in OECD Member countries as of January 1993, is a direct consequence of this instruction. In fact, it is the second report of this nature, succeeding "Economic Instruments for Environmental Protection" [OECD (1989a)].

This previous report presented information on the use of economic instruments in 1987, and the present report firstly adds a time perspective to this by looking at how the use of these instruments has developed over the past five years and what has been learned since then. Secondly, it deals with some new issues: i) it presents a first analysis of prospects for using economic instruments for environmental protection in economies which are in transition to becoming market based economies; ii) it attempts to review work done in the field of economic instruments for addressing regional and global environmental problems; and iii) it draws together recent work on the trade and environment issue.

1.1.3 Earlier OECD work on economic instruments

Some recent work in the field of environmental policy instruments by OECD has been referred to above: the 1989 first review and the 1991 Council Recommendations. In addition, reference should be made to OECD's recent study of the application of economic instruments [OECD (1991b)]. These studies and the positions therein have a firm footing in much earlier work done by OECD, going back to the very early days of environmental policy and environmental economics.

The growing severity and pervasiveness of pollution in the industrialized economies had led the OECD to elaborate, and in 1972, to adopt, the Polluter-Pays-Principle (PPP) as a background economic principle for environmental policy.

A next milestone was the OECD 1984 Conference on "Environment and Economics". At that conference the desirability of strengthening the role of economic instruments was emphasised, since they were expected to: (i) be efficient instruments; (ii) provide incentives for innovation; and (iii) be more appropriate when policy emphasis is shifting towards a more prevention oriented phase [OECD (1985)].

In several respects these ideas have been precursors to recommendations emanating from subsequent conferences and reports in other policy arenas, such as resource management [OECD (1989b)].

Currently, OECD is involved *inter alia* in developing views on economic approaches to the climate change issue [OECD (1992a and b)], in analysing the application of economic instruments to specific sectors such as packaging, in evaluating the distributional impacts of some economic instruments, and in a study on the fiscal issues related to ecotaxes [OECD (1993)].

The present review of the use of economic instruments is partly based on this past and current work.

1.2 "Sustainable development": a ground for wider policy relevance and support for economic instruments

Ever since environmental quality and sustainable resource use became areas of political concern (since the late 1960's), policy makers have searched for tools with which to achieve their objectives. Traditionally, the instruments employed were direct regulations such as, standards, permits, zoning, etc.

Many economists did advocate the use of economic incentives such as charges, subsidies, etc. [Baumol and Oates (1975)], but such voices were little noticed. It was not until the late 1980's before these ideas began to catch on in the field of environmental policy.

The presentation of the report of the World Commission for Environment and Development (the "Brundtland Commission"), *Our Common Future* [WCED (1987)] has marked the beginning of a new stage in international environmental policy. The Brundtland Commission was the first official international commission to adopt the notion of Sustainable Development as a prerequisite for continued societal existence. The way the notion was interpreted in the report implied an enhanced role for environmental economics in actual policy. WCED suggested a range of critical objectives for environmental and economic policies compatible with sustainability, including [WCED (1987), p. 49]:

-- reviving economic growth;
-- changing the quality of growth;
-- conserving and enhancing the resource base;
-- merging environment and economics in decision making.

The latter strategic imperative is subsequently described as the common theme throughout all other elements of this strategy (*ibid.*, p. 62). It is meant to induce a change in attitudes, objectives and institutional arrangements at all levels. In its discussion on the use of energy and materials, WCED advocates full (including environmental and resource) costing as a pricing policy (ibid., p. 217). Finally, when discussing strategies for sustainable industrial development, the use of economic instruments is explicitly advocated (*Ibid.*, p. 220 ff).

After the WCED report was published, the United Nations Conference on Environment and Development (UNCED) was announced. From the very outset, economic issues including the use of economic instruments, have been important in the preparation for that conference. Quite a number of other recent international declarations and policy statements have underlined their potential usefulness, including the Lankawi Declaration on Environment of the Commonwealth Heads of Government (Kuala Lumpur, Oct. 1989), the Bergen Ministerial Declaration on Sustainable Development in the ECE Region (May 1990), the Declaration of the Economic Summit (Houston, June 1990), the Conference on Environment and Development in Asia and the Pacific (Bangkok, Oct. 1990), the Ministerial Declaration of the Second World Climate Conference (Geneva, Nov. 1990), the Second World Industry Conference on Environmental Management (Rotterdam, April 1991), etc, (UNCED, PrepCom. A/CONF.151/PC/50, 1991).

Consequently, at UNCED itself a number of economically significant positions were accepted. To begin with, the fundamental importance of patterns of production and consumption in the industrialised market economies was recognised as a major contributor to environmental degradation. Second, the right of developing countries to continue to develop was underlined. The two together point to the need to redistribute access to the planet's limited "environmental space", and the need to use that space efficiently and sustainably. At various places in the main outputs of the conference there is recognition of the polluter (and user) pays principles, the need to internalise environmental costs, the precautionary approach to environmental change, and the use of economic instruments ("Declaration of Rio" and "Agenda 21"). Referring specifically to Principle 16: "National authorities should endeavour to promote the internalisation of environmental costs and the use of economic instruments, taking into account the approach that the polluter should, in principle, bear the cost of pollution", and Chapter 8 of Agenda 21: "What is needed is an appropriate effort to explore and make more effective and widespread use of (economic instruments) ..."(8.30), and "...Governments should consider gradually building on experience with economic instruments and market mechanisms ...to...establish effective combinations of economic, regulatory and voluntary (self-regulatory) approaches "(8.32).

In various regional settings, the notion of economic instruments appears to have gained support as well. For instance, the European Community in its Fifth Environmental Action Plan is proposing to broaden the range of instruments of environmental policy including an economic approach of "getting the prices right" [Commission of the EC (1992), Par. 7.4]. Targets and actions proposed include the further application of the polluter pays principle, and the introduction of a transparent system of pollution charges, deposit/refund systems, etc.

A final background factor worth mentioning, is the collapse of the centrally planned economies of Central and Eastern Europe, which reinforced an upsurge of sympathy for, and interest in, market-based approaches and market analogues to be used across a range of policy contexts. At the same time, there is a concern over the rapidity and the simplicity of this swing of the pendulum from command and control approaches, to market based mechanisms, also in these emerging market economies. To several economists working in the area of environmental economics, this has provided another rationale for analysing economic instruments and market based approaches to environmental problems (see Chapter 6).

1.3 Economic instruments: what are they?

1.3.1 The management of environmental impacts of economic activities

Economic activities generate several types of environmental pressures on the environment, such as:

a) input demands (*e.g.*, materials, energy, intermediate products);
b) pollution/waste flows;
c) spatial intrusions in natural areas, *e.g.*, by roads, etc.

Such pressures will to some degree be buffered by absorptive systems and processes (*e.g.*, waste assimilation, pollution absorption, resilience of ecosystems to disturbance, etc) and regenerative processes in the environment. If these pressures exceed the buffering capacities, then they lead to environmental change; if that change leads to a reduced capacity of the environment to satisfy human needs, then one can speak of environmental degradation.

Environmental degradation leads to policy responses in terms of for example, measures aimed at reducing environmental pressure or enhancing environmental buffering capacities. Environmental policy instruments are the environmental policy maker's tools in attempting to alter societal processes in such a way that they become and remain compatible with the policy maker's environmental objectives.

In seeking to ensure sustainable use of environmental resources and the maintenance of stricter levels of environmental quality, environmental policy can make use of (mixes of) two basic strategies (Fig. 1.1, approaches a and b):

a) engaging in public projects and programmes aimed at preventing, compensating and eliminating environmental degradation or at providing substitutes for traditional behavioural patterns, such as: collective treatment facilities; environmental sanitation and (re)construction programmes; new forests; bicycle paths and railway lines;

b) influencing the decision making process at the micro level, *i.e.*, that of the environmentally relevant (economic) agents such as consumers, producers, investors.

The second strategy is discussed in more detail below.

Rational decision makers will base decisions about their activities on a comparison of the various options. They will compare the costs and benefits of these options, as relevant to them. Costs and benefits here are defined as all (dis)advantages relevant to the decision maker, as aggregated by his/her individual weighting system. In such a situation, decisions can basically be influenced in three different ways. (Fig. 1.1, left hand side):

a) alteration of the set of options open to agents;
b) alteration of the cost and/or benefits relevant to agents;
c) alteration of the priorities and significance agents attach to environmental change (*i.e.*, altering the structure of agents' costs and benefits).

Approach b.1 involves providing new alternatives or forbidding (or licensing) old ones. Typically, this has been the approach followed by environmental policy in most industrialized countries. It has been called the 'command-and-control' approach. Instruments used in this approach have included a whole range of 'direct' regulations (*i.e.*, regulations directly influencing behaviour from an external "leverage point") such as: standards; bans; permits; zoning, quota, use restrictions, etc. These instruments present cases of *direct regulation*.

Direct regulations can be defined as institutional measures aimed at directly influencing the environmental performance of polluters by regulating processes or products used, by abandoning or limiting the discharge of certain pollutants, and/or by restricting activities to certain times, areas, etc, [OECD (1989)]. Their main feature is, that a specific level of pollution (abatement) is prescribed. The polluter is left with no choice but to comply with the regulation, or face penalties in judicial and administrative procedures.

Approach b.2 leads to the application of economic incentives or market stimuli. The motivation relied upon here is that if environmentally more appropriate behaviour is made more rewarding in the eyes of the agent involved, then attitudes and behaviour will 'automatically' shift in favour of these socially more desirable alternatives. Options can be made more or less (financially or economically) attractive by applying charges or levies, granting subsidies, implementing tax differentiation, etc. (see below for a more complete list). Such instruments are referred to below as *economic instruments*. In this way environmental concerns can in a certain sense be 'internalised' by altering the agent's context rather than the agent's value structure or preferences.

Approach b.3 entails approaches such as education, information extension, training, but also social pressure, negotiation and other forms of "moral suasion". Here the mechanism is a change of perceptions and priorities within the agent's decision framework, or, a full 'internalisation' within the preference structure of the agent. Internalizing environmental awareness and responsibility into individual decision-making is pursued by applying pressure and/or suasion either indirectly or directly.

One specific instrument in this category is that of voluntary agreements reached on the basis of negotiations between the environmental agency and private sectors.

These instruments could be referred to as *suasive instruments*.

Figure 1.1 Environmental policy approaches

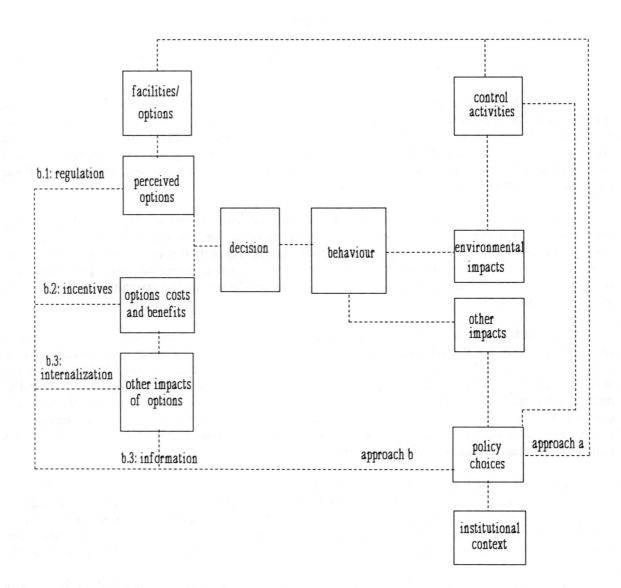

1.3.2   Definitions and enumeration of economic instruments

Instruments may certainly be labelled "economic" when they affect estimates of the costs and benefits of alternative actions open to economic agents. Their effect is to influence decision-making and behaviour in such a way that alternatives are chosen that lead to an environmentally more desirable situation than in the absence of the instrument. Economic instruments, in contrast to direct regulations, thus allow agents the freedom to respond to certain stimuli in a way they themselves think most beneficial. Indeed, if a certain environmental target is to be reached, economic instruments will at least in theory induce cost-effective behaviour.

Two questions relating to this definition are, whether this implies that economic instruments are financial instruments, and whether all instruments with a financial aspect are therefore economic? The answer to both questions is negative.

Some non-financial instruments (*e.g.*, trading schemes) of environmental policy may be aimed at achieving least cost methods of attaining certain ambient quality standards or overall discharge levels. In the above definition of economic instruments such instruments are included. Overlap with direct regulation may occur when market creation or provisions to enable interventionist behaviour are seen as institutional arrangements to influence indirectly environmental quality changes in relation to economic behaviour. Then, they are sometimes seen as direct regulation rather than as economic instruments. In fact they are true economic ones, given the definition above.

Direct regulation often has a financial or monetary component attached to it. The outcome of the regulation in terms of pollution discharge, may then depend on both technical and monetary considerations. In some cases the regulation is accompanied by charges that have no intended impact on behaviour, but in reality do affect it drastically. The above definition of economic instruments restricts this notion to instruments that have intended impacts on factual behaviour of economic agents by modification of costs and benefits as assessed by the actors themselves. Hence, many factual charge systems would not qualify as economic instruments under this definition.

A narrower definition is to consider an instrument as economic when in fact (and disregarding intentions), it has an observable impact on behaviour. Other descriptions refer to the involvement of money, with instruments often being seen as "economic" if there is a direct financial component. This definition would rule out recognized types of instruments such as emissions trading (see below). Again other descriptions would suggest that instruments are economic only if they use or simulate market-type mechanisms.

In other words, the notion of "economic" instruments has come to mean different things in different contexts and as perceived from different views of what economics is about. In consequence, the determination of whether or not an instrument should be dealt with in this report can not be made on the basis of a rigid definition, but will be made explicit by enumeration (see below).

1.3.3   Economic instruments : a classification

Basically, one may distinguish the following categories of economic instruments: i) charges, ii) subsidies, iii) deposit-refund systems, iv) market creation, and v) financial enforcement incentives, [OECD (1989a)]. Several subcategories are listed below. Borderline cases which exist are also indicated, as are the economic instruments reviewed in this report. As the previous section suggests, there is a certain amount of arbitrariness involved in this choice. Common elements in the instruments that have been selected, are:

a) the availability of alternative behavioural options;
b) the involvement of government (related) authorities;
c) the intention of (directly or indirectly) maintaining or improving environmental quality by applying the instrument.
d) an impact on levels of costs or benefits of alternative behavioural options.

The existence of financial stimuli (either negative or positive) is not one of the common elements, though it is almost always present.

In this report no attention will be paid to one major category of economic instruments, *i.e.*, subsidies. This has several grounds. To begin with, the overall orientation of the OECD approach to environmental policy as based on the Polluter Pays Principle is aversive of subsidies allowing for some well-defined exceptions. Another, more pragmatic, argument is, that in reality a very wide range of smaller or larger subsidy schemes with environmental relevance may be in existence, but it has proven to be rather difficult to obtain an overview [see *e.g.*, OECD (1989a)] and assess the situation. OECD has in fact reviewed the practices in Member countries on assistance (*i.e.*, subsidies) provided in relation to environmental improvement. Some conclusions reached were, that i) the value of the assistance (in absolute and relative terms) varies widely from country to country, ii) this value may not decline over time, but iii) the overall level of assistance is slight to negligible (< 0.1 per cent of GNP), though there may be larger sectoral distortions [OECD (1990)].

A general description and further breakdown of the various categories of economic instruments considered here, is set out below. Before presenting a detailed picture, two caveats are in order:

a) There is nothing inherently "good" about economic instruments as such and as we shall see, they may or may not have certain merits relative to other instruments;

b) Normally, instruments of environmental policy are not used in pure, isolated form. Typically, economic instruments are part of wider combinations, often used together with certain regulatory instruments. Most charges are linked with a permitting system, and trade in emission permits by definition occurs within politically determined boundaries.

Charges/Taxes

Charges may, to some extent, be considered as a "price" to be paid for pollution. Polluters have to pay for their implicit claim on environmental "services", which thereby enters at least in some part into private cost-benefit calculations. Charges may have an incentive impact and a revenue (or fund) raising impact. The incentive impact of charges depends on the cost and price changes brought about by the charge. In many cases, charges mainly have a revenue raising impact. They are too low to have an incentive impact and the revenues are intended for collective treatment, research on new abatement technologies or for subsidizing new investment.

Theoretically (as we shall see in section 2.4.3) charges need to be differentiated from taxes. Charges are associated with return flows of goods or services whereas taxes are not. In practice this distinction is difficult to make and maintain, and below we shall use charges, taxes and levies interchangeably. There are various types of charges:

- **Charges on emissions or effluent charges**

These are charges to be paid on discharges into the environment (or, in the case of user charges, into collective treatment facilities) and are based in principle on (a proxy of) the quantity and/or quality of discharged pollutants.

Emission charges may take the form of **"user charges"**. These are payments for the costs of collective or public treatment of effluents. Tariffs may be uniform or they may differ according to the amount of effluent treated.

Charges on emissions are among the economic instruments studied in this report;

- **Product charges or taxes**

These are charges or taxes on products that are polluting in the manufacturing or consumption phase or for which a disposal system has been organized. Product charges can be based on some product characteristic (*e.g.*, charge on sulphur content in mineral oil) or on the product itself (mineral oil charge).

One form which product charges may take in practice, is that of **tax differentiation** leading to more favourable prices for "environmentally friendly" products and vice versa. The sole purpose of tax differentiation is its incentive impact and this instrument often operates in a budget neutral manner, while product charges could also have a revenue-raising goal.

The use of product charges will be reviewed in this report.

- **"Administrative charges" (beyond the scope of this study)**

Apart from charges on emissions and products the 1989 OECD review also dealt with so-called administrative charges such as control and authorization fees and payments for administrative services. These are used, for example, in registering certain chemicals or implementation and enforcement of regulations. Administrative charges will not be analyzed in this survey.

In relation to charges, their intention as stated in the laws that they are based on, may be expressed in terms of their capacity to raise revenues (either for general public purposes or for specific, earmarked funds in the environmental policy domain) and/or in terms of their incentive impact on the behaviour of economic agents. Apart from the intentions of environmental policy makers, in this report attention must also be given to the actual impact of these instruments in the economic process. In order to provide as much clarity as is possible we shall categorise charges into four classes [c.f. OECD (1989a)]:

i) charges intended to have an incentive function and operating as such ("II-charges");
ii) charges intended to have an incentive function but operating mainly as revenue or fund raising ("IF-charges");
iii) charges intended to raise funds and operating as such ("FF-charges");
iv) charges intended to raise funds but with a substantial incentive impact ("FI-charges").

Deposit-Refund Systems

In deposit-refund systems a surcharge is laid on the price of potentially polluting products. When pollution is avoided by returning these products or any residuals to a collection system, a refund of the surcharge follows.

Deposit refund systems will be surveyed in this report. A distinction can be made between deposit refund systems, which aim at enhancing re-use, and return premia which provide an incentive for recycling. The survey intends to cover both types.

Market Creation

Markets can be created where agents might buy "rights" for actual or potential pollution or where they can sell their "pollution rights" or their process residuals (recycled materials). Several types exist:

- **Emissions trading**

In this approach, dischargers operate under some multi-source emission limit and trade is allowed in permits adding up to that limit. Such systems can also operate in cases of single source permits. If a discharger releases less pollution than its limit allows, the firm can sell or trade the differences between its actual discharges and its allowable discharges to another firm which then has the right to release more than its initial limit allows. Trades can take place within a plant, within a firm or among different firms.

This study will deal with emissions trading. The related concept of trading in quotas for resource use, is beyond the scope of this study.

Two types of market creation that in principle belong to the category of economic instruments of environmental policy will be briefly mentioned below, but will not be reviewed in the present study:

- **Market intervention**

Price intervention (subsidies in case market prices fall below certain levels) or *ex ante* price guarantees might create or facilitate the continued existence of a market. An example would be the case of potentially valuable residuals, those residuals either being dumped or offered for low-value treatment and re-use. Price interventions are quite similar to (negative) product charges which, however, are applied in already existing and well functioning markets. Price interventions are beyond the scope of this report.

- **Liability**

Legally establishing liability of polluters for environmental damage or clean up costs associated with emissions or the storage of wastes generated, may lead to the creation of a market in which risks for damage penalties are transferred to insurance companies. In so far as the establishing of liability is a matter for government, it could be called an instrument of environmental policy, albeit a judicial one rather than an economic one. In fact, such legislation would imply a different distribution of rights to environmental quality, and once established, an insurance market may automatically emerge. Premiums will reflect the probable damage (penalty) or cleanup costs and the likelihood that damage will occur. The incentive here is the possibility of lower premiums, when industrial processes are more secure or result in lower damage, less wastes or fewer accidents. It has been decided to consider this instrument as being beyond the scope of this study.

(Financial) Enforcement Incentives

This category of economic instruments is sometimes considered as a legal rather than an economic instrument. Noncompliance is "punished" either ex-ante (by asking for a payment returnable upon compliance) or ex-post (by imposing a fine when noncompliance is occurring). However, enforcement incentives may provide an economic rationale for compliance, when noncompliance is a seriously considered decision alternative. Enforcement incentives are therefore included in this study.

Two types are included in the survey:

- *Non-compliance fees* are imposed when polluters do not comply with certain regulations. The systems included here are those in which the rates are more or less proportional to non compliance benefits reaped or environmental damage inflicted.

- *Performance bonds* are payments to authorities in expectation of compliance with imposed regulations. Refunding takes place when compliance has been achieved.

1.3.4 Resume of types of economic instruments reviewed

In this study, then, we shall attempt to provide a comprehensive overview of the use of the following types of economic instruments of environmental policy:

a) charges/taxes on emissions;
b) charges/taxes on products;
c) deposit-refund systems;
d) tradeable permits;
e) enforcement incentives.

The terms of reference of this study rule out paying deep attention to subsidies. They are of course economic instruments but OECD has dealt with them elsewhere [OECD (1990)].

Also ruled out are "new" types of approaches slightly beyond economic incentives, but potentially with substantial environmental as well as economic significance, such as liability and voluntary agreements. In fact, on the latter (*i.e.*, voluntary agreements) work will be done in the OECD context.

Finally, this study pays little attention to areas such as resource pricing, and economic instruments in the field of resource management which are the subject of a separate project. Yet, at various points in this study there will be excursions into these territories.

1.4 The use of economic instruments in 1987

Defining economic instruments loosely, *i.e.*, including financial and fiscal instruments that may not have had the intention of modifying the behaviour of polluters and resource users, there have been economic instruments in existence for a long time. In OECD (1989a) a review is presented of the situation in the OECD Member Countries in 1987, yielding a total of 150 economic instruments (or over 10 per country surveyed), some of these having a history of decades. This total included a number of instruments that are beyond the scope of the present survey such as subsidies, administrative charges and liability which were reviewed in the 1987 survey. Exclusion of these leads to a total of nearly 100, or almost 7 per country surveyed.

The 1987 survey included some cases of interesting successes, such as the Dutch water pollution charge, some US experiences in emissions trading, and some deposit-refund schemes in Sweden. However, a closer look revealed that many of these instruments were of little significance and most of them were not really intended to have an incentive impact. One should thus not be deluded into thinking that OECD countries employed market based instruments on any significant scale, in 1987.

Looking at the (150) instruments identified and analyzed [OECD (1989a)], roughly 80 of these 150 instruments were charges, about 40 were subsidies and the remainder were other types such as deposit-refund systems and trading schemes. Looking at the various economic instruments in terms of what their purpose was and how they actually performed (in both cases, either providing an incentive or raising revenue), one finds that in terms of the numbers involved, less than half of the economic instruments reviewed had the intention of generating an economic incentive and over half were meant to raise revenue. Only one third may have effectively had some incentive impact.

Basically then, in 1987, environmental policies in the OECD Member countries were command-and-control policies with some financial and economic add-ons. Chapters 3 and 4 will reveal to what extent this has changed since then.

1.5 Structure of the project and the report

1.5.1   The project: objectives and approach

The OECD Project on economic instruments deals with the actual and potential use by OECD member countries, of a number of environmental policy instruments as enumerated above. In addition, the project is to explore the actual and potential use of these instruments in the economies in transition to becoming market economies.

Other important issues to address in this project are: i) the relationship between environmental policy to trade issues and trade policy via economic instruments; and ii) economic instruments for addressing so-called global environmental problems such as climate change. The report is to provide a review of current positions vis-a-vis these issues.

The operational approach followed has been to:

a) Carry out a survey in 1992, of the situation on the use of economic instruments as per 1st January 1993 and put this situation into perspective by comparing it with the situation in 1987 [OECD (1989a)]; extract lessons from countries' experiences with the various instruments applied;

b) Execute on a consultancy basis case studies on the potentials for using economic instruments in some of the economies in transition;

c) Study the literature on economic instruments in the area of global change with a focus on OECD's work in this field;

d) Analyze the trade implications of environmental policy instruments.

1.5.2   *The structure of the report*

Part I of the report presents the economic and policy background for economic instruments. Chapter 2 of Part I is devoted to providing further background on policy and economic aspects relevant to understanding the emergence and the development of economic instruments in environmental policy. Chapter 2 also draws some lessons from recent reflections of the contextual influence on the appropriate set of environmental policy instruments - the policy context as well as the context of application. The reader familiar with the discussion on economic instruments in economics and in political science may skip most of chapter 2, and jump to sections 2.4 and 2.5 immediately.

Part II presents the results of the survey of the current use of economic instruments, and an analysis of these against the 1987 situation are presented in chapters 3 and 4. An attempt to draw lessons from the practical experiences underlying the use of operational economic instruments is reflected in chapter 5. In a sense, these three chapters are the empirical part of this report.

Several significant related issues and extensions are dealt with in Part II. Chapter 6 presents an overview, as complete as was possible, on economic instruments as they figure in policy documents on and analyses of environmental policies in a number of economies in transition. Also, it pays attention to what these economies might be able to adopt from the OECD experience with economic instruments. It turns out that due to huge differences in context, extrapolation from OECD experiences to recommendations to environmental policy makers in the economies in transition, is not a simple process and in fact may not be possible in certain cases.

Part III deals with the international dimension of economic instruments. Chapter 7 reviews the state of the art of developing economic instruments for dealing with global environmental issues, focusing on the recent discussion on charges and trading schemes. Attention is given to some new in-between, partial and "hybrid" schemes suggested as practical next steps towards a situation in which more pure, general, and effective approaches could be in place. Chapter 8 deals with the trade-related problems of using economic instruments.

Part IV proposes conclusions and explains prospects on the use of economic instruments. In the final chapter (chapter 9), conclusions on all elements of the 1992/3 project on economic instruments are presented together with this study's implications for further work (by OECD and other bodies) in the future.

References

BAUMOL W.J. and W.E. OATES (1988), *The Theory of Environmental Policy*, Cambridge University Press, Cambridge.

COMMISSION OF THE EC (1992), "Towards Sustainability: a New Community Programme of Policy and Action in Relation to the Environment and Sustainable Development, Proposed by the Community, March, Brussels.

OECD (1985), *Environment and Economics*, OECD, Paris.

OECD (1989a), *Economic Instruments for Environmental Protection*, OECD Paris.

OECD (1989b), *Renewable Natural Resources: Economic Incentives for Improved Management*, OECD, Paris.

OECD (1990), "Financial Assistance Systems for Pollution Prevention and Control in OECD Countries", OECD, Environment Monograph. No 33. Paris.

OECD (1991a), "Recommendation of the Council on the Use of Economic Instruments in OECD, *Environmental Policy: How to apply Economic Instruments*", OECD, Paris.

OECD (1991b), *Environmental Policy: How to Apply Economic Instruments*, OECD, op.cit..

OECD (1991c), "Environment Committee at Ministerial Level: Communique", Printed in: WICEM Second World Industry Conference on Environmental Management, Rotterdam 10-12 April 1991, *Conference Reports and Background Papers*, International Chamber of Commerce Lysaker No.

OECD (1992a), *Climate Change: Designing a Practical Tax System*, OECD, Paris.

OECD (1992b), *Climate Change: Designing a Tradeable Permit System*, OECD, Paris.

OECD (1993), *Taxation and Environment: Complementary Policies,* OECD, Paris.

UNCED (1992), "Recent International Declarations and Policy Statements Relating to the Utilisation of Economic Instruments (Extracts)", UN/UNEP A/CONF.151/PC/50, Annex 2.

Chapter 2

Economic Instruments, Policy Contexts and Economic Analysis

2.1 Introduction

2.1.1 *Externalities and institutional failure*

It is well established that economic activities may lead to effects that are external to those who decide over these activities in the first place and may thus generate social costs (including the costs of environmental degradation) that are not fully translated into private costs.

The issue arises therefore of how to reach the social optimum under such circumstances. Pigou (1920) advocated the internalisation of these and other externalities through a centrally imposed system of bounties and taxes. Baumol and Oates (1975) have developed more practical charges to attain cost effectiveness, sidestepping the issue of Pareto-efficiency. Alternatives to this system of charges are, decentralised approaches via property rights [Dales (1968), Tietenberg (1988)] and/or bargaining [Coase (1960)]. From 1960 onward, especially since 1975, a vast literature on the theoretical merits and demerits of these and other approaches for dealing with environmental externalities has emerged (for a review, see Bohm and Russell (1985)]. A first broad review of empirical applications was published by OECD [OECD (1989b)].

Environmental degradation is not just an incidental and unwanted result of some minor deficiencies in the economic process. Rather, its roots may go as deep as, among other things, the decision making mechanisms at work within the economic process and the social and political forces that operate on it. We refer to these mechanisms and forces as the institutions governing the economic process.

There may also be barriers in the way to adoption and implementation of effective environmental policies. Some of these barriers are frictional (*e.g.*, when new policies imply a rearrangement of costs and benefits), others are structural (when underlying causes of unsustainability are inadequately addressed or curbed).

An important structural mechanism contributing to the unsustainability of economic development can be that of *institutional failure* to respond to the emerging environmental realities [see for example, O'Riordan (1981); Opschoor (1990); Lang *et al* (1991)]. The next subsection looks at several types of institutional failure. A subsequent subsection will present, in resume form, what notions have come forward from standard environmental economics to deal with these failures.

2.1.2   Structure of Chapter 2

This chapter attempts to deal with the questions of why and when economic instruments promise to be effective and efficient ways of dealing with environmental problems, by addressing the following points:

a)   institutional failures as sources of environmental problems (section 2.2);
b)   the role of economic instruments vis-a-vis these failures and the influence of contextual and implementation related aspects (section 2.3);
c)   some dynamic elements in environmental policy (section 2.4).

A final section (2.5) will summarise where we are in terms of why and when to use economic instruments and what new insights have emerged since 1987.

2.2   Environmental degradation and institutional failure

Institutional failures are one set of potential triggers of environmental degradation and therefore of unsustainable development. In searching for patterns of change of (*inter alia*) institutions (c.f. the Brundtland definition of sustainable development, WCED (1987) :46) so as to make economic development ecologically viable, it is thus important to analyze and reduce (or even remove) institutional failure.

It is convenient to refer to the "failure" of institutions wherever they induce or favour decisions that lead society away or prevent society from achieving a socially optimal allocation of resources.

The most frequently cited institutional failures are *market failures* and *government failures* (see fig. 2.1 below).

2.2.1   Market failures: cost shifting

The degradation of the environment is the product of the independent decisions of billions of individual users of environmental resources and the determinants of these decisions such as, the available information on the environmental effects of resource use, preferences of consumers and the technology available to producers, the rate at which users discount the future effects of current actions, the property rights that define their endowments, the set of relative prices that determine market opportunities associated with those endowments, the cultural, religious and legal restrictions on individual behaviour that prescribe the range of admissible actions, and so on. While the decisions of resource users may be privately rational given these elements, they sometimes appear to be socially damaging - *i.e.*, they may compromise the interests of present as well as future generations. Typically in market economies the decisions of these resource users are co-ordinated by market forces.

2.2.2   Definition and types of market failure

Market failure can be defined as the inability of the market to lead the economic process towards a social optimum. One main aspect of this is the failure to encapsulate in costs and prices the external effects, or reductions in utility and profits, that agents other than those directly involved in market transactions and the activities associated with these, have to undergo. In relation to environmental goods and services one may point at the externalities related to pollution, resource exploitation and ecosystems' intrusion. Market failures thus entail a failure of the market, as an institution, to allocate resources in the best interest of society. The main categories of such failure are:

a) failure of markets to emerge - particularly for the environmental effects of economic activity and

b) failures of existing markets.

In relation to market failures of type b), Button distinguishes i) internal market failures and ii) external market failures [OECD (1992e)]. Internal market failures can be related to i1) the nature of the goods exchanged (*e.g.*, collective goods or "club goods") or i2) the structure of supply (*e.g.*, monopolistic or oligopolistic structures). Internal market failures may also be the result of i3) the dynamics of the market (*e.g.*, instability of solutions). We would like to add that i4) lack of information or knowledge may lead to socially sub-optimal situations. Market failure is labelled "external" when externalities exist, even when the market is functioning without internal failures [see also OECD (1992f), pp 29 and 65ff]. In the field of environmental and resource issues, we are concerned with each of these types and subtypes of market failure, though particularly with i1), i4) and ii).

Impediments to resolving market failure

It is useful to distinguish between two types of externality. Reciprocal externalities are those in which all parties having rights of access to a resource are able to impose costs on each other (as often happens with resources in common property). Unidirectional externalities are those in which processes in the common environment ensure that the short run external environmental costs or benefits of resource use are 'one way' (for example, deforestation by the users of an upper watershed inflicts damage on the users of the lower watershed). Both types of externality give rise to "cost shifting" or "displacement of costs" [Kapp (1950); Pearce and Turner (1990); Opschoor (1989)]. But these different types of externalities may require different strategies or instruments to internalise them.

Reasons why "external" interests are not adequately internalised, may include:

a) Insufficient legally based "property rights" or "access rights" protecting the damaged party, or inadequate liability/accountability regulations enforceable upon the causal agent;

b) Lacking the means to exert "countervailing power" (Galbraith) through the market place (i.e. lack of purchasing power) or otherwise (lack of influence on legislation on rights, liability and on processes such as standards setting, zoning etc.).

Reasons why this situation is not easily changed by installing more appropriate institutions or legislation, include "filtering" processes in responding to claims for institutional change towards a more sustainable development, for *e.g.*, the filters of time preference (whereby future effects and future interests are discounted away), and of present purchasing (and voting) power.

2.2.3 Government failures

Government failure can be said to arise in two cases: i)"intervention failure" or inappropriate actions of government, whether deliberate or not [see *e.g.*, Button in OECD (1992e)]; and ii) failure due to lack of intervention by government or failure to correct for market failures. In the case of intervention failure, internal and external market failure may be the result. In the case of lack of interventions, existing market failures are left to prevail. Government failures occur when the end result of political and administrative processes is that prices are leading away from the social optimum, for reasons entrenched in the institutional system. Very often, government failure ensues from interventions in other policy sectors. Examples in the environmental field include protective agricultural policies leading to over-production, subsidisation of large scale energy users, etc.

2.2.4 Types of intervention failures

Intervention failures as defined above, can be divided into *policy failures* and *administrative failures* [Lang *et al* (1991)].

The term *policy failure* refers to the range of regulatory instruments, fiscal, exchange rate, monetary, price, income and other policies (including environmental policy) which distort the private cost of environmental resource use so as to make it privately rational to damage the social heritage. One may speak of policy failure in two rather different cases.

a) Where prevalent policies (relating to sectors other than environmental and resource management) are based on decisions in which ecological or environmental considerations were given insufficient weight. This very often is the case with sectoral policies where sectoral interests and powers have predominated over, or excluded ecological considerations, or with policies dating back to periods of time when environmental problems were not yet perceived fully. Examples are, policies in the areas of agriculture, energy, transportation [for the latter see OECD (1992e)].

b) When environmental and resource policies inadequately address the social and ecological repercussions of economic activity (for failures related to the management of wetlands and forests,[see OECD (1992f)].

The notion of *administrative failure* refers to a range of problems within the organization of government at the various levels, leading to inadequate policy implementation. Examples include, rigidities due to entrenched traditional divisions of labour within administrative organizations (very often along sectoral lines), insufficient integration between agencies and departments, lack of instruments or mandates sufficiently strong to achieve policy objectives, lack of instruments or powers to ensure policy implementation within the economic processes.

In the following we indicate some environmentally relevant failures in sectoral and other policies. The other types of government failure mentioned, *i.e.*, those of administrative failure and lack of intervention, will not be further elaborated upon in this report.

Sectoral policies

Past sectoral policies (*e.g.*, in the field of energy, agriculture and transportation) have often been decided upon primarily with the sectoral interests in mind, at best with some consideration for trade offs vis-a-vis other sectors. Environmental concerns have not, or not yet, been appropriately internalised. Moreover, decision makers have limited time horizons and/or discount future consequences of present decisions. Thus, policy formation may suffer from biases towards stronger (in terms of economic and political power or significance) sectors and against interests that cannot manifest themselves on current markets and in today's political arena, such as future generations' interests.

Sectoral policy failure often results in the subsidisation of sectoral activities. In resource related sectors such as agriculture, water, timber and energy, this leads to artificially low resource prices [see OECD (1992f) on wetlands and forest resource management]. In such cases, users of the products of these sectors are paying less than the social costs their use gives rise to. They thus are induced to consume more than would be the case were the price corrected for social costs. Prices then give the wrong signals and the sector may expand to levels beyond what is socially desirable.

Other policies

This paragraph could in principle deal with quite a number of policies, however discussion is restricted here to some of the more important ones that are not the subject of explicit discussions elsewhere in this report. Later on, attention is paid to taxation issues and trade issues. Here, macro economic policies and price policies in particular are the focus of attention.

a)   Macro-Economic Policies.

Economic growth may be beneficial for obvious reasons, mostly having to do with the welfare it enables. Economic growth may also be consistent with the maintenance of environmental quality, and is certainly feasible over some finite time horizon, as for example the OECD project on the economy and the environment [OECD (1985)] and several subsequent economic studies have shown. However, given a finite resource base, and finite waste absorptive capacity, an overall and global growth maximisation strategy might not be sustainable in the long run [*e.g.*, Perrings (1987)]. Current macroeconomic policies may suffer from potential policy failure in so far as long term environmental effects are ignored. The risk is that the global society will be confronted with environmental costs that are either irreversible (*e.g.*, species extinction) or very costly to redress (*e.g.*, the impact of pollution in Northern Bohemia or deforestation in tropical zones). From a long run perspective the levels of economic activities may have to be controlled and redirected to timely correct for this policy failure. This might be the case if changing the technologies or locations of our activities, would not provide sufficient responses to the ecological challenge.

b)   Price policies

Perhaps the most environmentally significant of the policy failures are those which drive a wedge between the true social cost of resource use, and the cost to the individual user - the private cost of resource use. There exists a range of fiscal, exchange rate, price and income policies which have the effect of encouraging the over-utilisation of environmental resources.

2.3   Economic instruments and institutional failure

2.3.1.   The welfare-economic promise

If the economic process will not automatically move the economy towards a socially optimal allocation, then the question arises as to how to address this problem. Standard economic analysis has suggested two basic avenues: i) private negotiations and legal action, or ii) policy intervention directly aimed at an alteration of market prices (*e.g.*, through charges), or redefining and altering the structure of property rights (*e.g.*, by licensing, zoning, standards, etc).

Figure 2.1 **A typology of institutional failure**

Market failures:

- Market absence

- Performance failure:

	- internal:	collective goods, market power, dynamic performance
	- external:	reciprocal, unidirectional

Government failures:

- Lack of intervention

- Intervention failure:	- Policy failure:	environmental policy, sectoral policy, macroeconomic policy,price policy etc.
	- administrative failure	

The first avenue suggested above, that of private actions, has as its point of departure the work of Coase (1960). He suggested that a bargaining approach might suffice in reaching a social optimum. Polluters and victims of environmental degradation are assumed to negotiate about the optimal level of environmental degradation or of economic activity giving rise to it, on the basis of their marginal damage costs and abatement costs. The mechanism assumed by Coase to operate, is the following. Left unregulated or in the absence of countervailing power from damaged parties, a polluter will try to operate at the level of activity where his profits are maximised. The social optimum is where the marginal profits are equal to the marginal damage due to the pollution. If the victim has legal rights to an unpolluted environment, then it could pay the polluter to compensate the victim . There allegedly is a "natural" tendency to move towards the social optimum. This is also assumed to be true in the case where the rights are with the polluter and the victim pays the polluter for abstaining from his activities. The "Coase Theorem" in fact claims that regardless of who holds the property rights, there is an automatic tendency to approach the social optimum via bargaining.

If this mechanism could be trusted to operate adequately in real world situations, then government regulation of externalities would be redundant. Implicit in the analysis is, that intervention would be necessary only if the costs of reaching a bargain (the "transaction costs") prove to be too high for an efficient solution to arise without it. These transaction costs include a range of elements difficult to measure such as, the cost of information on the nature and extent of environmental damage and treatment costs, costs of identifying, finding and addressing the relevant parties (both the polluters and the pollutees) or appropriate representatives of these, the cost of convincing them to reach a mutually acceptable agreement or the cost of litigation, etc.

However, a number of criticisms of and complications with the Coasian approach have been identified and testify to the need for policy intervention. These include the lack of realism of various assumptions underlying the analysis such as the alleged market perfection, the level of transactions costs in actually achieving negotiation and bargaining on the level of pollution, and difficulties in identifying and mobilising the relevant polluters and sufferers [Pearce and Turner, (1990); Barde (1992)]. There are thus many reasons why bargains do not, and cannot easily, occur. In their absence, there is a case for Government intervention.

In fact, environmental policies by governments can be regarded as remedies for situations with high transaction costs and compliance/enforcement costs in the absence of such policies. Hence we proceed by looking into some theoretical possibilities for policy interventions, *i.e.*, the second avenue suggested above.

Standard economic analysis not only suggests particular types of interventions including so-called economic instruments, but it also has provided a framework with which one could theoretically compare and evaluate a number of (first and second-best) instruments from points of view inherent in economic analysis, *i.e.*, allocative efficiency (incl. cost-effectiveness) and dynamic efficiency.

In 2.3.1 we will present what economic analysis has contributed in these respects. In 2.3.2 we review some of the problems that economic theory up till now has not been able to resolve. The upshot of it all is that a much broader approach is needed, including a proper treatment of several "contextual aspects" having to do with the policy context and the application context relevant to environmental policy instruments.

Allocative efficiency of intervention

There are several basic types of intervention, namely, standards, taxes/charges, trading approaches, negotiation for agreements. These are discussed below.

a)   Taxes/charges and standards

Pigou had advocated government intervention through the imposition of a tax on polluters based on the marginal (external) damage costs and the marginal abatement costs. The tax should induce polluters to automatically move to a socially optimal situation in terms of production and pollution abatement. However, in most cases it is impossible for an environmental agency to tax the pollution precisely at the appropriate level due to lack of adequate information on damage. The Pigovian solution has thus proven to be an impracticable one.

"Proxy solutions" to this problem have been proposed, such as emissions charges aimed at realising some specified level of reduction of emissions [Baumol and Oates, (1975)], or a "standard". Charges then would at least equalise the level of marginal pollution abatement costs among firms, and thus provide an incentive for the most cost-effective total investment in pollution clean-up.

One could regard the Baumol-Oates charge as a second-best alternative to the Pigovian charge, with Government allegedly making some assessment of where the socially optimum emissions reduction objective might be located, based on an implicit social valuation of (marginal) environmental damages.

Charges tend to be a lower-cost method of achieving a given standard or emission level, than a uniform standards policy if marginal abatement costs differ between sources. Moreover, they will provide a stronger incentive to firms to identify and even develop clean technologies with lower marginal abatement costs, as the financial reward of doing so exceeds the benefits of a standards based approach (at least in cases of rising marginal abatement costs).

b) Trade in emission rights

Marketable permits offer the same promise of efficiency as Baumol-Oates charges. By giving the polluters a chance to trade their pollution emission/discharge permits, the total cost of pollution abatement to some predetermined acceptable level, is minimised. As long as polluters have different costs of abatement there is an automatic market, with low-cost polluters selling permits and high-cost polluters buying them. Trading ensures a cost-effective total abatement result [see, however, Atkinson and Tietenberg (1991) and par.2.3.2].

For emission permit markets to function well, they have to meet a number of conditions [see *e.g.*, Tietenberg (1988); Pearce and Turner (1989); Barde (1992)]. Listed are the more important ones. First, like in the case of charges, there have to be significant differences in marginal pollution abatement costs and technological options for cleaner production must not have been exhausted. Second, the market must be characterised by sufficiently large numbers of buyers and sellers. Third, the importance of the location of both sources and receptors must be of relatively minor importance. Fourth, the rules governing the permits market must be simple and transparent.

Stavins and Whitehead (1992) have compared the advantages and disadvantages of pollution charges and tradeable permits. They observe that while permits set the level of control, charges establish the marginal costs of control. Permits allow a total pollution level to be set but cannot control pollution abatement expenditure. If the pollution context is one in which threshold effects in terms of damages (human health, etc) are known to be present, then permits may have a comparative advantage. Because charges do not control the actual level of pollution abatement they are better suited to situations in which damage impacts are fairly certain and relatively constant over a certain range, as well as situations in which small changes in abatement costs cause significant changes in production levels. In addition, there may be advantages and disadvantages having to do with the acceptability of the various alternatives. Tradeable permits could be seen as more compatible with standard economic practice (*e.g.*, by industry) than charges. Permit markets could, however, be complex in administrative terms, and the conditions determining their functioning may not all be met in reality (eg., in terms of the number of market parties and hence their relative market power, or in terms of their proximity).

c) (Voluntary) Agreements

One other form of intervention is that of negotiation between government or the environmental agency within government on the one hand, and (representatives of) polluters on the other. This may take the form of so-called "voluntary agreements" negotiated between the environmental agency and sectors of society, *e.g.*, industries, consumer organisations, etc. The agreement will be on short and medium term changes in patterns of investment, technological change, consumption, waste treatment, etc. These voluntary agreements may at first sight resemble negotiation and bargaining as described earlier, but there are important differences. First, this type of negotiation does not normally involve the exchange of environmental quality against financial transfers. Second, the damaged or potentially damaged parties do not participate in the negotiations. One could regard the role of governments in these voluntary agreements as taking place on behalf of society at large including the sufferers from environmental degradation. As in the case of the Baumol-Oates charge, government might be assumed to seek an approximate social optimum on the basis of some estimate of the marginal external damage costs. Also because these negotiations tend to be at the macro-meso level and tend not to be detailed enough to take into account locational aspects (of sources as well as receptors), this voluntary agreement is a second-best proxy only, but still one that could be better, from a point of view of effectiveness as well as efficiency, than that of no intervention. A full assessment would have to include an evaluation of government's capacity to approximate true social costs, enforcement and compliance aspects associated with the agreement, and the costs of reaching and implementing it.

Dynamic efficiency of intervention

The above arguments have focused on allocative efficiency in the full sense of that phrase, or on cost-efficient approaches to predetermined environmental objectives or constraints set by environmental policy. However, standard economic analysis has more to suggest by way of ideas on the usefulness of economic instruments.

In a dynamic setting, environmental policy instruments have an impact on both the degree of technological innovation and the process of diffusion (or penetration) of new technology. Charges (as well as trading in emissions permits) in theory carry a dynamic incentive effect. They are assumed to augment the process of technological change almost by definition, as charges will always stimulate an interest in technologies that reduce pollution and the obligation to pay charges at a cost that is lower than the otherwise paid charge. Moreover, charges may not only induce an interest in end-of-pipe provisions that firms can operate at a cost lower than the charge, but also that they will wish to develop or buy inherently cleaner technologies that in practice often prove to reduce normal production costs as well. Standards or non-tradable permits would lack this facility, often referred to as "X-efficiency" or "dynamic efficiency".

2.3.2   The problems

By the end of the 1980's, it had become clear that much of the original debate on economic instruments had remained too remote from the realities of the economic process and the policy arena. A more pragmatic approach appeared to be needed to modify the rather sweeping generalisations and expectations to more moderate proportions. Such an approach should recognise that differences in policy context and historical backgrounds and in operational elements related to implementation, are involved. Some of the main criticisms were:

a)   Economic analyses do not always convincingly reflect economic realities. Real markets do not always work as theory assumes. This point has to be given some credit, as empirically based doubts vis-a-vis the alleged dynamic efficiency would suggest (see below);

b)   Non-economic instruments may work equally well or even better than economic incentives. This point too has validity since the efficiency and effectiveness arguments associated with economic instruments are not always applicable, as a review of the history of environmental policy instruments discloses (below);

c)   Economic instruments cannot be as efficient as was claimed above, as the analysis by-passes a number of implementation issues (see the examples given of contextual issues, below);

d)   Economic analyses and recommendations often ignore or play down realities typical of the political "arena" (Majone) in which (environmental) policy is shaped in reality. One aspect of this is the issue of the distributional implications of environmental policy and instruments choice.

With allocative and cost efficiency, it must be realised that financial and economic instruments provide an incentive the significance of which depends on the elasticities that operate on behaviour (price elasticities, substitution elasticities, income elasticities), on the strength of the signal given (*e.g.*, the level of a charge), and on the availability of substitutes or alternative actions. Sometimes even high charges alone will not have sufficient behavioural significance and hence their environmental effectiveness is low, or dubious. Most charges introduced so far in OECD member countries have proven to be too low to have an incentive impact even if this were intended.

A significant feature in understanding the performance of specific economic instruments may be the market process they have to operate within or give rise to. A good illustration is that of market failure in cases of tradeable permits [Atkinson and Tietenberg (1991)]. It is by now recognised, that the cost savings due to US EPA's emissions trading programme have been substantial, but nowhere near cost-effective. As Atkinson and Tietenberg report, the cost savings have been smaller than expected and so has the trade volume. This can be explained at least in part by the dynamics of the actual trading process which is characterised by a sequence of bilateral trades (rather than multilateral and simultaneous, as is often assumed in theoretical models) and by the factual constraints on information about market opportunities available to the relevant agents. A closer look at the trading system under such conditions reveals also that a disproportionately high number of trades have been internal (within one corporation) [Atkinson and Tietenberg (1991)]. Markets as induced or implied by economic instruments may thus themselves be far from perfect.

A further aspect is that of the non-linearity of relevant phenomena such as, for example, abatement cost curves. There may be indivisibilities giving rise to discontinuities in responses to variations in, for example, charge levels.

As regards dynamic efficiency, some qualifications are called for as well. Up till now, the impact of the various policy approaches on factual patterns of innovation and diffusion of environmentally friendlier technology is still a matter for empirical analysis [Georg and Jorgensen (1990)] and debate. At least two features typical of the process of innovation have to be taken into account.

Firstly, in a context of uncertainty, innovation is more often than not the result of firms' market based interactions with others (clients, suppliers, etc). These interactions produce multiple influences on the products' and processes' environmental performance 'upstream'. Pure efficiency considerations can, in such circumstances, only play a limited role

Secondly, diffusion-promoting activities will influence these decisions. Innovation must then be seen as the outcome of a complex process within a "structure of cooperation". Depending on, for example, the level and type of innovation (process or product) and the actors involved, different policy instruments may provide different stimuli resulting in different environmental impacts.

Empirical evidence as far as it exists, casts some doubts on the dynamic efficiency of *e.g.*, effluent charges [Georg and Jorgensen (1990)]. They may have sizeable effects only in so far as firms with significant waste loads are affected, evasion by illegal dumping can be prevented, and the charges can be taylor-made to generate incentives to innovate in the appropriate directions.

Performance of other instruments

In the past, all countries' environmental policies (including strongly market oriented ones such as the USA) entailed the use of direct regulations in a "command and control" strategy [OECD (1989b)], *e.g.*, permits, zoning, standards. Governments have typically set standards (technology or performance based) for classes of industry or so-called scheduled processes across industrial categories. Direct regulation can relate to the behaviour of individuals and organisations, to plants or to equipment, to processes as well as to products. The basis for this type of control is some form of legislation. Compliance is mandatory and often sanctions for non-compliance exist.

While the standards approach is biased against technological innovation (*i.e.*, it provides no direct incentive for regulated polluters to exceed their prescribed target level of abatement) it still proves to be relatively attractive to control agencies. The reason for that is, that it does provide a measure of "certainty" of the policy result in terms of environmental effectiveness (as long as there is adequate monitoring and enforcement). This certainty [the most obvious advantage of direct regulation - OECD (1989a)] is particularly important when persistent and toxic substances are being released into the ambient environment [Opschoor and Pearce (1991)].

Other advantages of regulation are [Bohm and Russell (1985)]:

-- authorities' traditional familiarity with this approach;
-- its directness in comparison with *e.g.*, economic incentives that in fact change only the conditions under which economic agents decide on their activities;
-- regulatory instruments are not perceived as selling a right to pollute, contrary to charges and tradeable permits;
-- polluters may prefer them over economic instruments, as especially firms often assume they have more influence on regulations than on *e.g.*, charge levels, and as charges are additional to compliance costs.

From this, one must conclude that non-economic instruments do have a strong raison d'être. In fact, they still dominate the instruments selected, and very often economic instruments are used merely as adjoints to regulatory approaches, in "mixes" the performance of which in terms of efficiency and effectiveness are preferred (if not actually better) than those of "pure' instruments, especially the purely economic ones. And there are good grounds for that. In other words, a shift from a regulatory approach towards one based on economic incentives only is unlikely to occur, nor would it be desirable. Combinations of instruments are preferable and within such "cocktails" economic incentives will have a crucial role to play.

Contextual aspects: application context

Basically, in the process of designing and implementing a policy instrument, one may discern external and internal elements. Internal elements are those that are important in understanding how an instrument might effectively function or operate within a given economic process and administrative context. External elements are those that are important in the social, political and economic "environment" of that process. External elements include the operative national and international economic, fiscal and environmental policies. Internal elements have to do with source-related aspects, as well as features of the environments and of receptors therein. The focus in what follows, is on some internal elements - the application context.

Situation-specific characteristics relevant to the choice of instruments include source-related aspects such as, the availability of substitutes, elasticity, the potential for technological innovation, differentiation in abatement costs, competitiveness, market structure related features. They also include impact-related issues such as the seriousness of environmental damage, local and temporal variation in linkages between emissions and impact, etc. The importance of these factors is triggering more pragmatic studies of the context-specific elements that may provide indications as to when to employ which types (or mixes) of instruments. The Dutch Scientific Council for Government Policy, in a recent report on environmental policy instruments [WRR, (1992)], has developed such a more extensive approach. In chapter 5 this approach will be used to arrive at a more practical and operational view of the selection of instruments.

One important aspect often ignored in the traditional approach to economic instruments is the fact that in economic life interventions based on specific types and levels of environmental degradation often imply interventions in complex product life cycles and materials chains. Moreover, in product chains environmental degradation in fact "accumulates" from the environmental impacts in the mining stage in which the inputs are extracted, via the impacts in the various stages of secondary to final production, to the environmental impacts of consuming these products and entering them into the waste segments of the product life cycle. For environmental policies to truly attempt to be efficient, an integrated "chain approach" should ideally be applied to products and associated processes, and it is in such a context that instruments choice should be placed (in addition to the other complications addressed so far). Integrated chain analyses and similar approaches can be the basis for product labelling as well. But returning to the issue of economic instruments, integrated chain analysis in a broader context could, at least in theory, provide insights enabling an assessment of the relative merits of emissions and (final) product charges and input charges.

Contextual aspects: political factors

Governments' choices of policy instruments have a strong political basis and may be governed by a variety of considerations, some more rational than others. To support an appropriate choice, instruments could be evaluated against a number of selection criteria. The set of criteria normally used, encompasses [*e.g.*, OECD (1989b)]:

a) Environmental effectiveness, *i.e.*, the extent to which the instrument succeeds in reducing environmental impacts, in relation to policy targets set;

b) Economic efficiency, *i.e.*, the extent to which the instrument economises on resources (use of capital, labour, materials and energy);

c) Acceptability, *i.e.*, the extent to which the instrument can be properly implemented and enforced without running into problems of non-concordance with existing regulations, principles and policies, or of resistance by target groups or indirectly affected agents, on the basis of allegedly unfair or unproportional burden-sharing implications (equity considerations). Chapter 5 provides a more extensive discussion of these selection criteria in practical terms. Here, some acceptability-related considerations are dealt with at a rather abstract level.

Until fairly recently, direct regulation was the almost exclusive strategy to address environmental issues. Several developments since the late 1960's or early 1970's may help explain why the subject of instrument choice has gained increasing prominence on the public agenda [OECD (1989b)]:

a) increasing (and empirically based) doubts as to the effectiveness and efficiency of (further) regulation. Also increasing enforcement problems and doubts about compliance with direct regulation, leading to a tendency of "deregulation";

b) budgetary constraints that most Governments had to face led to an interest in instruments with the promise of efficiency and "built-in" compliance, and a capacity to generate funding. Using environmental considerations as a rationale for imposing new charges proved to add to the legitimacy (at least in the eyes of a large section of the public) of what effectively boiled down to new taxation;

c) the growing belief in the beneficial properties associated with harnessing market forces.

Widespread and general as these tendencies may have been, the actual development of environmental policy instruments has followed different courses in different parts of the OECD region, due to the diversity of policy contexts prevailing in OECD member countries. There may be differences in:

-- general political outlooks, *e.g.*, on market intervention;
-- political environments in which individual countries operate (*e.g.*, EC, EFTA/Nordic Council, NAFTA).
-- political structures (federalism, etc);
-- administrative cultures and societal responses to (particular types of) intervention;
-- priorities attached to environmental problems and the public support for environmental policies;
-- basic tenets of environmental policy (*e.g.*, quality oriented or source oriented);
-- distribution of responsibilities for economic sectors (and environmental compartments) over ministries, policy levels and agencies.

Yet, the preference for a regulatory approach as the foundation of a system of environmental policy instruments is understandable from the point of view of political feasibility. One can see this as the result of dominant motives with several of the main groups of actors - government, industry, environmental organisations. Assuming rent-seeking behaviour, there is a rationale for regulatory approaches at least from the perspectives of industry and governments, possibly at the expense of consumers [Verbruggen (1993)]. In fact, the whole idea of rational choices between *e.g.*, charges and standards in a setting of seeking to achieve objectives by selecting the most efficient instruments may be misleading. Rather, in actual political processes decision-making may instantaneously address very complex "packages" of objectives, instruments, side-payments or other compensatory or mitigating measures, etc. Policy analysis shows that there may be grounds for assuming that the policy arenas in which *e.g.*, instruments for water and air quality policies were shaped, might not be conducive to incentive based approaches, but might rather favour regulatory measures as these are less likely to lead to unsettling conflicts between the parties involved [De Savornin Lohman (1993)].

Distributional aspects

One aspect of particular importance in the policy arena is that of distributional consequences of using alternative types of economic (or other) policy instruments. Distributional aspects are a very sensitive and politically relevant feature of economic instruments, as these instruments typically and visibly involve financial flows with price and cost implications. Obviously, regulatory instruments have distributional implications as well, but they are much less transparent. In fact, economists would argue that in many cases the distributional repercussions of regulatory instruments potentially are even larger than those of economic ones as the latter at least induce efforts to achieve efficiency.

Harrison has reviewed the state of the art with respect to the distributive effects of economic instruments [and how to measure them - OECD (1994)]. He finds among other things, that generally pollution control costs tend to be regressive (with relatively higher percentage burdens for lower income households). Pollution control benefits tend to be progressively distributed when measured in physical units but less so when measured in value terms. Environmental taxes tend to be regressive when measured against a "no regulation" benchmark.

Compensations for distributional effects may be necessary, not only on equity grounds, but also on pragmatic ones. Potential losers might block a shift towards socially more desirable instruments unless they are in fact compensated. Harrison also compares possibilities for mitigation and compensation related to different economic instruments. He finds that they are generally available and appear to be capable of dealing with the distributional impacts of new instruments [OECD (1994)].

Resume

The preceding two arguments (on application context and on policy context) show that political, institutional and even cultural developments may influence the process of articulation of environmental policy objectives and strategies, and of instruments selection. In order to understand the changes over time in instruments actually introduced, and in order to reasonably predict the directions of change in this complex area, one has to take into account tendencies and developments in the political context (such as the impacts integration into larger units such as NAFTA, EC, on standardisation, harmonisation or simple voluntary convergence in fields such as taxes, etc), developments in the application context (*e.g.*, the effects of larger scale causes of environmental problems, more and more dispersed sources, etc, on enforcement possibilities and compliance), changes in priorities between criteria for instruments selection (*e.g.*, the increased concern over efficiency and the stated preference for market conformity), etc.

The complexity of the field of instrument choice points at the necessity of a multi-stage approach in which actual feasibility studies on specific instruments follow after a (positive) analysis of a range of specific external and internal factors all having to do with policy contexts and contexts of application. This will be taken up again in chapter 5.

2.4 Dynamic features in environmental policy today

Some main lessons from the above are that there will be a need for evaluating prevailing sectoral and other policies, and for finding institutions and instruments capable of achieving a rebalancing of rights and powers, and of improving market mechanisms from the perspective of pollution prevention and resource management.

Sectoral policies, both national and international, will have to be reviewed in the light of the *user pays principle* and the *polluter pays principle,* in order to present the full price of the involved goods and services to those who enjoy them. Integration of environmental concerns into other sectoral policies needs to be reinforced. Also, macro economic policies will have to be scrutinised for their consistency with concerns over the sustainability of economic development.

There is a need to review taxation policies and its foundations. In so far as scarcity is one justification for choosing tax bases, most current systems turn labour into an over-expensive factor of production and this reinforces tendencies towards unemployment. Ecotaxes are based on differences in environmental pressure or resource claims, and may be a very useful addition to the set of fiscal instruments. They are an example of fiscal instruments with a potentially very powerful economic incentive impact towards environmentally friendly behaviour in consumption and production .

Basically, what is implied in the analysis of this chapter so far, amounts to an argument in favour of an alteration of rights such that environmental quality claims and existence rights (of species), etc, are recognised, coupled with compensations to be made by those infringing upon those rights. To start with, these compensations could result from an extension of the Polluter Pays Principle to not only the measures prescribed by environmental policy (see below), but to damage costs (including ecological damage). In the following sections it is therefore proposed to look first at developments in relation to policy principles and to then look at current trends in the area of policy integration and tax reform.

2.4.1 Environmental policy principles

The development of PPP in OECD

The growing severity and pervasiveness of pollution in the industrialised economies had led the OECD to elaborate, and in 1972 to adopt, the Polluter-Pays-Principles (PPP) as a background economic principle for environmental policy. The principle as then adopted, implies that the polluter should bear the cost of pollution reduction measures necessary to bring the environment to an "acceptable state" as defined by public authorities. Basically, PPP is a non-subsidisation principle. The Recommendations on the Implementation of the PPP (adopted in 1974) specifies that, as a general rule, Member countries should not assist polluters in bearing these costs, with some exceptions (related to industries where PPP would create severe difficulties, transition periods for countries otherwise facing socio-economic problems in consequence of their environmental policies, situations where no serious trade and investment distortions were to be expected). In other words, the PPP as it appears in the OECD Recommendations is a non-subsidisation principle. This was a deliberate choice, so as to preclude as much as possible distortions of international trade and investment patterns.

The origins of the PPP can be traced to welfare economic ideas expressed as early as the 1920's (by Pigou), which state that ideally prices of goods and services should reflect the full social costs including the environmental costs as related to pollution, resource exploitation and other forms of environmental degradation. Not including these cost elements in the price formation on the market would lead to over-utilisation of resources and pollution to higher levels than are socially optimal. Prices should "tell the truth" on the costs of producing and consuming goods and services [Von Weiszacker (1989)]. Making the polluter pay is one way of internalising these environmental externalities. It is a way that could be considered "economically efficacious" or desirable [Barde (1992)]. This notion should not be confused with that of judicial liability or responsibility. PPP declares the polluter (whoever that is according to national legislation) to be the *primary accountable* agent, but the principle does allow these agents to pass on to their customers as much as they can, given market conditions, their environmental costs. PPP has been described by environmental economists as an institutional manifestation of the opportunity cost principle [Siebert (1981)]. It allocates the equivalent of the benefits foregone by pollution to those agents that cause it. It can be applied once environmental quality targets have been established by environmental authorities.

PPP as discussed so far, can be applied through the use of financing charges, compensation or liability schemes, etc, as practical vehicles for ensuring the reflection of full social costs in prices. In most cases however, PPP has typically been implemented by direct regulation based on standards, permits, etc, as it clearly imposes the costs of meeting the standard on the polluter.

Several points are left unspecified in the OECD elaboration of PPP [Barde (1992)]. To begin with, there is no explicit definition of which agent is to be regarded as the polluter. Decisions on that are left to the national authorities. Next, there is no specific indication as to how much the polluter should pay. The latter point will be returned to implicitly below, when the extended PPP is discussed.

Thoughts on PPP as a practical policy principle for OECD member countries have developed since 1972 [OECD (1992d)].

In 1989 the OECD adopted a Recommendation on the Application of the PPP to Accidental Pollution. This in effect links the economic principle and the legal principle relating to damage compensation. The 1991 Council Recommendation on the use of economic instruments in environmental policy also emphasises the necessity to internalise damage costs. These two Recommendations may eventually lead to a specification of PPP which extends beyond the costs of (preventive) measures and includes damage costs ("extended PPP"). At present, the Recommendation on accidental pollution renders the polluter accountable for the costs of measures to prevent accidents, measures to limit and contain the damage after an accident has occurred, and the costs of cleaning-up and decontamination operations [OECD (1989a)]. It does not include damage cost.

Currently, OECD is investigating the question of how the PPP could be applied to global pollution issues such as climate change [OECD (1992 a and b)].

More recently, policy agencies such as the EC have agreed that environmental quality can be achieved and maintained by a variety of measures and procedures (regulation, taxes, charges, state aids, permits, agreements). The choice of instruments is now seen as depending on circumstances, administrative and legal frameworks, the nature of the environmental problem to be tackled etc, rather than as a matter of principle.

Notions of an "extended" PPP have created support for the idea that polluters should also pay for pollution below the levels compatible with an acceptable state of the environment, as the environmental capacity to absorb waste is scarce. PPP could be used to integrate utilisation of the environment (including its waste assimilation capacity) into the economic sphere through price signals via economic instruments such as pollution charges and permits [OECD, (1992d)].

PPP on a global scale?

Effective international environmental policy requires a coordinated approach because environmental regulations may become a source of trade distortion if some countries subsidise private investment in pollution control while others do not. Hence there is a need to coordinate at the level of policy principles and PPP is a very appropriate candidate for that, as it is already accepted and implemented in a substantial part of the world economy.

In this respect it is important to note that the Declaration on Environment and Development of Rio de Janeiro (June 1992) has established that "national authorities should endeavour to promote the internalisation of environmental costs and the use of economic instruments, taking into account the approach that the polluter should, in principle, bear the cost of pollution, with due regard to the public interest and without distorting international trade and investment" (Principle 16). This amounts to the adoption, at least in principle, of the PPP as one basis for global environmental policy, and offers hope for the adoption of the principle, notably in the economies in transition (see chapter 6) and the developing countries.

A further step to be considered would be to promote the recognition by the General Agreement on Tariffs and Trade, of the need to adopt, as a basic tenet of international economic relations, the PPP as a social cost internalising principle (see also chapter 8).

Further extensions and other policy principles

An extension of PPP discussed increasingly is, to regard resource use as falling within the scope of it, *i.e.*, "the polluter and user should pay", or "P(U)PP". Resource pricing is one area next to that of pollution control, where prices do not reflect the full social costs of exploitation. Most notably, the so called user costs are often disregarded [OECD (1989a)]. In the next section, under policy integration, we shall summarise some recent contributions to the discussion on resource pricing.

Other principles are emerging besides the P(U)PP. For instance, the European Community has adopted three relevant principles that have economic significance and may have some bearing on economic instruments:

-- the *prevention or precautionary principle*, which explicitly recognises the existence of uncertainty (environmental and social) and seeks to avoid irreversible damages via the imposition of a safety margin into policy. It also seeks to prevent waste generation at source, as well as retaining some end-of-pipe measures. Economic incentives qualify well in the light of this principle (even if their performance in this respect has yet to be established firmly);

-- the *economic efficiency/cost effectiveness principle*, applying both to the setting of standards and the design of the policy instruments for attaining them;

-- the *subsidiarity principle*, to assign environmental decisions and enforcement to the lowest level of government capable of handling it without significant residual externalities.

The precautionary principle is also reflected in the Rio Declaration on Environment and Development: " In order to protect the environment, the precautionary approach shall be widely applied by states according to their capabilities...lack of full scientific certainty shall not be used as a reason for postponing cost-effective measures to prevent environmental degradation" (principle 15).

It is to be expected, that new principles based on, for example, solidarity, accountability for previous environmentally relevant behaviour, cost-effectiveness and/or collective interest or responsibility for the future, will come to be developed and discussed with a view to perhaps partly replace the old PP(U)P adagium. Such new principles would also need instruments and transfer mechanisms of a financial and/or economic nature. One may think of extending the notion of subsidies in the form of transfers of capital and know-how -- side-payments to induce international acceptance of environmental policy principles and/or strategies. One may think of such subsidies as originating from funds created on the basis of pollution related charges (*e.g.*, acidification funds), or on income based international taxation (*e.g.*, GDP related systems), etc. Several developments in factual environmental policy (*e.g.*, ideas on "joint implementation", debt-for-nature swaps, etc.) indicate that there is increasing recognition of the need to develop views on the desirability, domain and scope of a "Victim Pays Principle" in the area of global environmental policy (see also chapter 7). It is proposed that such a principle could allow for transitional and level of income related side payments only, as intermediate steps towards, and in the context of a recognised prime position of the PP(U)P.

2.4.2 Policy integration and resource pricing

Environmental issues very often are related to developments and policies in other areas. The interdependence between environment and, *e.g.*, agricultural, transportation and energy policies is apparent. Policies in such areas can generate price signals that interfere with the internalisation of environmental and resource costs. Another relationship is the indirect effects of developments in one sector on the performance of another, due to environmental quality change.

Sectoral activities (such as agricultural activities) are based on different mixes of factors of production including environmental resources (natural resources, absorptive capacities for handling pollution, and space). The notion of maintaining the resource base as a precondition for a sustained use of them in future economic development, has become a central national and international policy objective.

Three general and inter-related aspects of the sustainability goal have been identified [OECD (1993a)]:

-- the intergenerational welfare aspect, where the central goal is to maintain a certain environmental stock or its equivalent for future generations;

-- the "proper pricing" aspect where private and public decision processes must be based on ("shadow") prices reflecting the social opportunity costs of using resources;

-- the preservation aspect where non-substitutable resources or environmental assets should be preserved and irreversible damage to such environmental assets should be prevented.

Some illustrations

Let us take agricultural policy as one particular illustration. The relationship with the environment is obvious, in terms of claims on natural resources and space, and in terms of claims on absorptive capacities or other buffers against environmental pollution. In recent years policies on sustainable agriculture or "sustainable agriculture and rural development" have been explored and discussed [*e.g.*, FAO (1991)]. A recent review of agricultural and environmental policy integration [OECD (1993a)] concludes that there is indeed a noticeable increase in the number of policies with an explicit or indirect environmental objective, often as add-ons to existing agricultural policies. Simultaneously, environmental policies have increasingly reached out to the agricultural sector (*e.g.*, pesticide control, policies addressing non-point sources of pollution). The review concludes that in terms of policy integration there is a change of attitudes but it still is too early to evaluate the impact, thus "it would be unwise to...exaggerate the extent of real integration that has been achieved" [OECD (1993a), p. 14]. The review proposes a number of priorities for action in this field of policy integration, including a better analysis of the possible use and impacts of economic policy instruments and direct regulations, including taxes, user charges, direct payments, etc. Related to this, is the key importance of arriving at correct market prices for agricultural inputs (*e.g.*, by removing explicit subsidies for some fertilisers, enhancing transparency in *e.g.*, water use pricing, and by applying the PPP) as well as outputs (*e.g.*, by removing production distorting and trade distorting measures).

A second illustration directly refers to an environmental asset rather than an economic activity, integrated coastal zone management. Coastal zones in many OECD countries (and elsewhere) are under severe stress from urbanisation, extended recreational activities, pollution, etc, such that resource

44

allocation conflicts in these areas are increasing [OECD (1993b)). Coastal resources manifest themselves within, and are often the products of, natural ecosystems and their ongoing supply requires these systems to be managed on a basis of sustainable yields. Moreover, these resources interact (and so do the related ecosystems). This and the multiple use characteristics of coastal zones renders them susceptible to conflicts. Finally, there are institutional issues such as the optimal types of supply (private, or public) or mixes thereof. Coastal zone management thus poses a number of problems of policy integration and strategy.

The instruments currently used in coastal resource management are typically those of regulation and control (notably, land use zoning). Economic instruments are increasingly being used [OECD (1993b), p. 13]. Given the fact that it is difficult to value coastal zone assets properly, economic instruments should always be used within, and complementary to a regulatory framework. The study concludes that most OECD countries lack comprehensive coastal zone management mechanisms and coordination. Appropriate, more integrative administrative mechanisms are to be developed as well as appropriate mixes of instruments (including economic ones).

Resource pricing

Already in the 1980's, OECD has carried out work in the area of water pricing policies and practices [OECD (1987)]. It was recommended that the use of economically efficient pricing mechanisms should be considered (based on marginal social costs). The "User pays principle" was also put forward, the essential element being that this would provide to the user an incentive to economise in the use of the resource. Under the "user pays" regime as proposed, subsidisation by taxpayers and cross-subsidisation among water service users would be abolished (unless special reasons exist for their retention) [OECD (1987), pp. 15-17].

It is by now accepted that in pricing environmental resources one should distinguish between the use of a resource as such (*e.g.*, water or coal) and the indirect claim (by *e.g.*, polluting the environment) on absorptive systems of buffering systems operating in the environment. In the latter case, emissions charges may be appropriate, whereas in the former case one could ideally apply user charges (or product charges, in the absence of a proper set of resource prices). Such user charges may be labelled "input charges" when they relate to resource inputs into production chains.

Basically, natural resources should be priced in such a way that the cost of extracting or harvesting the resource, as well as extraction-associated externalities and "user cost" elements is met [Pearce and Turner (1989)). User costs are the benefits foregone by consuming a resource now rather than leaving it for future consumption. Economic instruments (and direct regulation, defined and allocated property or access rights, etc) may help in arriving at a situation where prices better approximate their socially desirable level.

Where are we?

This section suggests that the progress made in the area of policy integration is far from adequate in terms of a factual merging of environment and economics in the policies of related economic sectors and the management of involved environmental resources. In theory one may be able to indicate what socially optimal prices are, but this leads to qualitative suggestions as to how to correct prices, rather than to concrete and convincing quantitative indication. Mechanisms to translate external cost elements into price corrections exist, and economic instruments are potentially important ones.

2.4.3   Taxation and the environment

With the emphasis on sustainable development, environmental and economic policies cannot be separated. Previous sections in this chapter bear witness to that, and to the fact that such integration is now indeed emerging. This is also reflecting itself at the instrument level. There is an increasing use of economic instruments such as charges and in some OECD countries one can observe the emergence of environmental taxes. This takes place against a background of reform of the tax systems in a number of OECD countries [OECD (1993c)). Indeed, one important area of policy integration is that of environment and taxation.

One main element in recent tax system reforms has been a trend away from using these systems to achieve specific economic or social objectives, in favour of a neutral system (in terms of these objectives). This reflects a growing preference for relying on market forces where this is appropriate (*i.e.*, in the absence of market failure).

The increasing political support for environmental policy will lead to more use of economic instruments and may raise the interest in environmental taxes. To the extent that these would be compatible with the Polluter (and User) Pays Principle, such a move could be considered to be in line with the general trend mentioned above, that they imply corrections of market signals in the appropriate direction.

In theory there is a distinction between charges and taxes. Charges are payments for which a good or service is rendered in return (more or less proportional to the amount paid), and taxes are payments on the basis of *e.g.*, the level of pollution for which no direct return in terms of goods or services is given. In practice it is difficult to maintain this and in the remainder of this report the terms environmental charges and taxes will be used without these connotations in mind. Taxes in the strict sense have a revenue raising objective, normally for the general public budget, whereas charges or levies as an economic instrument may be considered mainly for their allocative impacts.

Under the broad term "environmental tax" one may discern:

-- emission based taxes;
-- indirect taxes on goods and services or differentials in such taxes on environmental grounds (*e.g.*, differentiated value added rates), either originally intended as such, or meanwhile being used in this way (*e.g.*, fuel taxes);
-- tax allowances related to direct taxes *e.g.*, corporate profit taxes, in cases of certain types of environmentally desirable (investment) behaviour.

The road ahead

Taken in a broad sense, environmental taxation now occurs in fields such as, transportation, fuels and other energy sources, agricultural inputs, water use, waste management, air pollution, etc. [OECD (1993c)].

The Task Force on Taxation and Environment studied the options of, and problems associated with environmental taxation [OECD (1993c)]. In some areas or circumstances, environmental taxes would be basically inappropriate, such as in cases of dangerous toxic pollutants. Environmental taxes, if they are to effectively affect price signals, could be considered for use in situations of reversible environmental impacts. As taxes, they may suffer from the disadvantage of uncertainty with respect to their revenues. Economic agents confronted with environmental taxes may decide to change their behaviour to such a degree as to affect revenue levels. This uncertainty may be a transitional problem only. Other difficulties are the complexity of some environmental taxes and the political resistance they may generate.

New environmental taxes should preferably be in accordance with accepted policy objectives and with taxation principles such as equity, neutrality and administrative efficiency. Making fiscal and environmental policies compatible and mutually reinforcing may imply the removal of certain hidden subsidies embedded in present tax systems. OECD (1993c) (Chapter 8) proposes guidelines with respect to the introduction of environmental taxes. Some important ones relate to a "combined strategy" where environmental taxes are part of a package that has a higher degree of acceptance (see Section 2.3.2. above), progressive or "step by step' implementation (see also chapter 6 below), and simplicity. With respect to the latter, it is important that fiscal incentives are as closely linked to the pollution which the tax aims to control, without demanding that this linkage is complete and direct. PPP does require however that there is as close a link as is possible and administratively feasible.

Environmental taxation also has an international dimension. National tax reforms involving the introduction of environmental taxes are often claimed to affect industries' competitive positions. This issue may be important and should be addressed in the design stage of an economic tax, but its significance is often exaggerated [OECD (1993c), Chapter 8]. Secondly, there are the transnational environmental problems and the policies to address these. If taxes are to be an element in such policies, a co-ordinated introduction of such measures may be instrumental in obtaining acceptance especially from the business communities. Whether taxes could be used in areas such as global warming abatement, will be discussed in chapter 7.

The potential for introducing environmental taxes in the economies in transition will be discussed in chapter 6.

2.5 Some conclusions

Environmental degradation leads to policy responses in terms of *e.g.*, measures aimed at reducing environmental pressure or enhancing environmental buffering capacities. Environmental policy uses a range of instruments to realise these objectives. From a recently concluded international academic project on economic instruments [Opschoor and Turner (1993)] and based on the analysis in this and the previous chapter, the following summing up of the state of the art is derived:

1. Environmental degradation has its roots in the economic process (notably, its relation to types and levels of economic activities, and their development), but also in the way decision making on economic activities and policies has been institutionalised. Conditions pertaining to the institutions that direct the economic process from within (*i.e.*, the market and "market failure") are such that government interventions are needed to ensure the incorporation of environmental externalities.

2. A range of types of interventions is available including, direct regulation, economic incentives and suasive or voluntary solutions (including negotiation).

3. The effects of policy instruments depend on the economic, political and administrative context in which they are applied. There has been a tendency to analyze instruments in ideal-type form and in a generic fashion (*e.g.*, "the" efficiency and effectiveness features of product charges). However, the complexities of the interactions between environmental and economic

processes, as well as the dynamics of innovation preclude straightforward and simple broad brush recommendations on instruments. Rather, context-specific and often complex (*i.e.*, mixes of elements of command and control, incentive and suasive natures) instruments will have to be developed. Unfortunately, policy instruments are still too much studied in isolation from real life interdependencies such as their product-cycle environment. Tools need to be developed and applied that deal with these aspects from an integrated chain perspective.

4. Assuming a "rational" approach, policy makers would select instruments so as to achieve their objectives in an optimal manner (that is, with reference to criteria such as effectiveness and efficiency) and with reference to the 'concordance' of instruments with current political trends or policies (*e.g.*, compatibility with principles such as "the polluter pays"), societal acceptability, compliance/enforcement aspects, etc. Whether this assumed rationality of the process of instruments selection is indeed appropriate, is a matter for empirical research, but environmental economics can contribute by feeding that process with information on the basis of their analyses of the short and long term effectiveness and efficiency, indirect effects (on *e.g.*, trade and investment, trade-offs with other policy objectives, and institutional appropriateness). Referring to the set of criteria for evaluation of alternative instruments, the approach should focus on, i) environmental effectiveness, ii) economic efficiency, and iii) acceptability in terms of, for example, concordance with institutional frameworks, distributional impacts and administrative feasibility.

5. The potential policy relevance of economic instruments for environmental policy is by now well established and no longer rests on theoretical or academic arguments only. The call for increasingly stringent environmental quality standards in the short run inevitably means rising policy-response costs and therefore enhances the appeal of cost-effective market-based instruments. Economic instruments are potentially relevant in policy contexts that are based on a preventative approach.

    Economic incentives appear to operate best in combination with, or in support of, other instruments such as direct regulation. Economic incentives alone will not effectively and/or efficiently deal with environmental problems, whether national or international ones.

6. Environmental economics must go beyond estimating the effectiveness and efficiency of environmental policy instruments, as their political acceptability cannot be understood from these points of view only. From, for example, the perspective of the theory of public choice, preferences for non-economic instruments as often expressed by economic agents, can be explained to some degree by assuming rent-seeking behaviour of polluters. But in order to explain the process of instruments choice one must even go beyond these perspectives, *i.e.*, context-specific frameworks for instruments selection need to be developed (see end of Par. 2.3.2). In developing such tools, a distinction between source-related and pollution-impact related characteristics is useful.

7. (Semi-) quantitative performance criteria to evaluate environmental policy instruments are now standard research practice. They cover effects or impacts on, i) environmental quality, ii) sectoral and national levels of production or productivity and employment, iii) income, consumption, purchasing power or welfare, iv) investment and relocation, v) administrative costs and revenue flows, vi) effects on income distribution, sectoral income shares, etc, vii) cost levels, profitability and competitiveness, (viii) international trade and balance of trade impacts.

Qualitative performance criteria used, include, i) acceptability, ii) legality, iii) compatibility/concordance with policy principles.

8. There is a need for at least considering harmonisation of countries' instrumental approaches when international trade and investment patterns are likely to be affected.

9. Existing regulations and policy interventions may create a setting in which efficiency-based consideration of environmental policy instruments would at best indicate second-best solutions. Internalising externalities via economic instruments may not make much sense in a world of seriously distorted markets (*i.e.*, in a complex situation involving multiple market and government failures).

10. The impact of charges and other economic incentives on the rate and direction of innovation is a much claimed advantage of such instruments but actual outcomes are not yet sufficiently well documented. There is a risk on the side of the regulator, however, that more interventionist policy may stimulate the 'wrong' technological trajectory.

11. PPP has become an increasingly well established principle likely to gain even more ground in future. Furthermore, it is developing in various directions. Its scope has sharpened and has extended to broader ranges of environmental policy. However, the exact extent to which damage costs are, or should be included, has yet to be established.

All these developments provide at least a better breeding ground for the development and use of economic instruments. The 1989 review concluded that PPP actually enhanced the use of standards and some revenue raising financial instruments, rather than the full range of economic and financial incentives [OECD (1989b)]. This need no longer be the case.

Moreover, it is to be expected, that new principles, for example based on solidarity, past accountability, cost-effectiveness or future collective interest, will have to be developed to complement the maxim of polluter or user pays. The "victim pays" option and conditions under which it might be made operational as a principle, are to be elaborated,albeit in the overall context of a fundamental Polluter and User Pays approach.

12. Options for integrating environmental considerations in other sectors' policies are far from having been exhausted. In fact, OECD countries are now witnessing the beginning of such integration efforts. Economic instruments and generally instruments that bring market signals closer to their socially desirable levels, have important roles to play and this insight has increasingly become common.

Environmental taxation may be one specific area in which this policy integration can take place.

What is new since 1989?

This chapter is closed by presenting some views as to what developments there have been since the first survey on the use of economic instruments [OECD (1989b)].

The most striking development has been the growth in the interest in the subject, theoretically, empirically and in terms of policy interest.

Although the empirical work still is in its early days, progress has been made in the development of tools to gauge impacts and indirect consequences of new policy instruments. There is a need to extend this work especially in the direction of integrated chain approaches and in incorporating other elements of the context of application (see par. 2.3.2).

Partly based on that literature, but also as a result of more detailed studies outside of mainstream environmental economics, there is much less dogmatism or rhetorics in the dialogue on environmental policy instruments. A pragmatic approach is beginning to prevail, in which one no longer is categorically in favour of, or against certain types of instruments, and in which the interest is in realistic assessments of the pros and cons of different mixes of instruments in the specific policy contexts and application contexts within which they are to operate.

Environmental policy since the end of the 1980s has become more interested in tackling environmental problems at higher spatial levels, such as continental and even global problems. At that level there certainly is much less scope for a command-and-control approach and hence economic instruments become more interesting options. Environmental policy has also become more interested in diffuse and mobile sources, which are again types of sources for which economic instruments provide effective approaches.

The need for policy integration has become, if anything, more visible and a major development is the growing interest in environmental taxation and ecotaxes.

Finally, the debate on environmental policy instruments is drawing global interest and appears to be embarking on new avenues in order to accommodate the demands of international environmental policies in a world of differences in terms of levels of development and access to resources.

References

ATKINSON S. and T. TIETENBERG (1991), "Market Failure in Incentive Based Regulation: the Case of Emissions Trading", *Journal of Environmental Economics and Management* 21:17-31.

BAUMOL W.J. and W.E. OATES (1988), *The Theory of Environmental Policy*, Cambridge University Press, Cambridge.

BARDE J.-Ph. (1992), *Economie et politique de l'environnement*, Presses Universitaires de France, Paris.

BOHM and RUSSELL (1985), "Alternative Policy Instruments", In A.V. Kneese *et al.*, (1985), *Handbook of Natural Resource and Energy Economics*, (Vol. 1), North Holland, Amsterdam.

DIETZ F.J. and W.J.M. HEIJMAN, eds. (1988), *Environmental Policy in a Market Economy*, PUDOC, Wageningen.

KAPP K.W. (1950), *Social Costs of Private Enterprise*, (paperback ed 1971), Schocken Books Inc, New York.

OECD, (1972), Council Recommendation on Guiding Principles Concerning International Aspects of Environmental Policies, 26 May 1972 in, *The Polluter Pays Principle*, Environment Monograph, OECD, Paris, 1992.

OECD (1987), *Pricing of Water Services*, OECD, Paris.

OECD (1989), Council Recommendation on the Application of the Polluter Pays Principle to Accidental Pollution in, *The Polluter Pays Principle*, op.cit

OECD (1990), *The Economics of Sustainable Development: a Progress Report*, OECD, Paris.

OECD (1992d), *The Polluter Pays Principle*, *op. cit.*

OECD (1992e), *Market and Government Failures in Environmental Management: the Case of Transport*, OECD, Paris.

OECD (1992f), *Market and Government Failures in Environmental Management: Wetlands and Forests*, OECD, Paris.

OECD (1993a), *Agricultural and Environmental Policy Integration: Recent Progress and New Directions*, OECD, Paris.

OECD (1993b), *Coastal Zone Management: Integrated Policies*, OECD, Paris.

OECD (1993c), *Taxation and Environment: Complementary Policies*, OECD, Paris.

OECD (1994), *The Distributive Effects of Economic Instruments for Environmental Policy*, OECD, Paris.

OPSCHOOR J.B. (1990), "Economic Instruments for Sustainable Development", In, Anon. (1990) *The Conference Report*, Conference: "Sustainable Development, Science and Policy", NAVF, Bergen 1990: 329-342.

OPSCHOOR and TURNER (in press), *Economic Incentives and Environmental policies: Principles and Practice*, Kluwer Ac. Press, Dordrecht.

OPSCHOOR J.B. and H.B. VOS (1989), *Economic Instruments for Environmental Protection*, OECD, Paris.

O'RIORDAN (1981), *Environmentalism*, Pion Ltd, London.

PEARCE D.W. and R. K.TURNER (1990), *Economics of Natural Resources and the Environment*, Harverster Wheatsheaf, New York/London.

PERRINGS C. (1987), *Economy and Environment*, Cambridge, CUP.

PERRINGS (1990), "Economic Growth and Sustainable Development", In, Anon, (1990), *The Conference Report*, Conference: "Sustainable Development, Science and Policy", NAVF, Bergen 1990.

PORTNEY P.R., ed. (1990), *Public Policies for Environmental Protection*, Resources for the Future, Washington DC.

SAVORNIN LOHMAN, A. de (1993), "Economic Incentives in Environmental Policy: Why are they White Ravens?", In, Opschoor and Turner (in press).

TIETENBERG T. (1988), *Environmental and Natural Resource Economics*, Harper Collins, USA.

VERBRUGGEN H. (1993), "Environmental policy failures and Environmental Policy Levels", In Opschoor and Turner (in press).

WEISZAECKER E.U. von (1989), *Erdpolitik: Oekologische Realpolitik an der Schwelle zum Jahrhundert der Umwelt*, Wissenschaftliche Buchgesellschaft, Darmstadt.

World Commission on Environment and Development (WCED) (1987), *Our Common Future*, Oxford University Press, Oxford.

PART II

ECONOMIC INSTRUMENTS IN PRACTICE

Chapter 3

Economic Instruments in OECD-Countries: A Survey

3.1 Introduction

3.1.1 Contents of the survey

The survey reports policy instruments effective on January 1st 1992 in OECD-countries.

In addition "proposals" have been included, *i.e.*, instruments due to take effect on or before January 1st 1993. In the text these proposals have been put between parentheses, *e.g.*, (France) in Table 3.2.

For countries with a federalized administrative structure (Australia, Belgium, Canada, Germany and the USA) the survey is primarily addressed to policy instruments at federal level. Data on policy instruments applied at sub-federal level have been included, but no comprehensive coverage is claimed. In the text instruments applied at sub-federal level are indicated with the subscript "reg" (regional), *e.g.*, Canada$_{reg}$ in Table 3.1.

This chapter presents the results per instrument. Chapter 4 will provide an overview and compare the outcomes of the present survey with the preceding survey [Opschoor and Vos (1989)].

3.1.2 Method of data collection

For this survey, questionnaires have been sent to all 24 OECD member countries. The questionnaires have been returned by contact persons of 13 member countries. Data have been gathered from the replies to the questionnaires, from reactions to a draft version of this chapter that has been circulated and from documents submitted by OECD-member countries to the Group on Economic and Environment Policy Integration. In addition to these sources a number of publications have been utilized that are listed in Appendix I to this chapter.

3.1.3 Definition of economic instruments

The survey is on instruments that are explicitly in the domain of environmental policy. Therefore policy instruments that are primarily intended for other purposes, and that may, or actually do, have environmental side effects, are not included. For instance, general excises on car petrol have not been included, unless rates for leaded and unleaded are differentiated. General excises on energy products are outside the scope of this survey.

As was explained in Chapter 1, the survey covers the sub field of environmental policy that is normally indicated as "pollution", not the sub field of "resource use". For instance, policy instruments in fishery management are not included.

The coverage of this survey is different from the previous survey [Opschoor and Vos (1989)]. Subsidies are not included. Administrative charges, "market intervention" and liability are not included. Enforcement incentives (non-compliance fees and performance bonds) have been included only if their rates are not fixed but proportional in some way, to environmental damage inflicted or non-compliance benefits reaped by the polluter.

There are various ways of subdividing the category of charges. In this report the subdivision is based on the item on which the charge is levied, either emissions or products.

The category of "user charges" does not refer to the item charged, but to the spending of revenues. Revenue of user charges is spent on collective treatment of effluents. User charges are levied in water pollution, waste removal and processing policies on actual emissions, or a proxy of that. Within the logic of this survey they are a subcategory of charges on emissions (3.2).

Different from the previous survey, tax differentiations have been included in product charges.

The survey reports on the following policy instruments:

- Charges on emissions (3.2) - These have been subdivided according to environmental compartment: air, noise, soil, waste, water.
- Charges on products (3.3)
- Deposit refunds (3.4)
- Tradeable permits (3.5)
- Enforcement incentives (3.6)

3.1.4   Reporting format

Data material on charges are reported, if the data material allows it, in a standard format. The format includes, charge base and rate, incentive effects (intended and actual) and revenue spending.

The available evidence on incentive effects of charges is reported in a separate column "Incentive", subdivided into "Int" (intended) and "Act" (actual).

Whether a specific charge has been intended as an incentive instrument has been deduced from its rate, or from intentions expressed by policy makers in policy documents.

With actual incentive effects the "+" category applies if either formal research has demonstrated incentive impacts or if environmental impacts have been achieved that cannot be accounted for by other factors.

In reporting about actual incentive effects the "unclear" category applies to cases where there is some, but inconclusive, evidence of incentive effects. For instance if a charge is applied in conjunction with other policy instruments, it is difficult to identify separately the effects of the charge and the accompanying policies.

For deposit refunds the reporting format includes the item on which the deposit is levied, the deposit rate (in absolute terms and as a percentage of market price) and the return percentage.

Charge rates are expressed in ECU's. Exchange rates on January 1st 1992 are listed in Appendix II.

3.2 Charges on emissions

This section reports on charges that are levied formally on emissions of polluting sources. Sources are firms and households. The charge base is either:

-- Actual source emissions, *i.e.*, emissions that are actually metered - For instance, the emissions on which the Swedish NO_x charge are levied (3.2.1) are actually measured.

-- A proxy of a source's emissions - For instance, aircraft noise charges (3.2.2) are all levied on the basis of pre specified aircraft characteristics serving as a proxy for actual noise emissions. Also user charges for sewerage and sewage treatment are generally levied on water consumption, serving as a proxy for wastewater emissions.

-- A flat rate - For instance, municipal waste charges for households are generally levied at flat rates with each household paying a fixed sum, unconnected to the quantity of waste actually supplied.

3.2.1 Air pollution

The Canadian permit fee, that functions from July 1st 1992 in the Province of British Columbia, is based on emissions of pollutants as allowed in permits. Fees are reduced if applicants can demonstrate that actual emissions are below permitted emissions. When actual emissions exceed permitted emissions, a new permit has to be issued and fees revised accordingly.

The French charge is levied on a limited category of installations. Qualifying installations include, burning installations with capacity over 20 MW, waste incinerators with capacity over 3 ton/hr and installations emitting over 150 ton/yr of acidifying pollutants. The charge has a redistributive purpose. Revenue is spent on subsidizing pollution abatement investments at the charged installations. The present rate of ECU 19.0 will be increased to ECU 25.3.

In Japan the SO_x charge is based on actual emissions, with rates differing substantially between regions. The levy is partially based on SO_x emissions between 1982 and 1986, at a rate of ECU $0.65/Nm^3$, partially on emissions in the previous year at the rates indicated in the table.

In the USA Title V of the revised Clean Air Act authorizes States to levy emission charges as a condition for permit, from 1-1-1993 onwards.

Table 3.1 **Charges on air pollution**

Country	Charge base and rate	Incentive Int	Incentive Act	Revenue spending
(Canada$_{reg}$)	Permit fee for air pollution	-/+	..	Air quality control
France	Acidifying emissions: ECU 19.0/ton (SO_2, NO_x, H_2S, N_2O, HCl)			
Japan	SO_x-emissions: rates differ regionally, between ECU 0.5-4.5/Nm^3	+	#	Compensation of health damage
Portugal	SO_2, NO_x	..	..	Air quality control
Sweden	NO_x-emissions of energy producers: ECU 4.7/kg NO_2	+	+	Rebated to energy producers
(USA)	Criteria pollutants, $> =$ ECU 16.4/ton	-/+	..	Air quality control

Notes: Key to symbols:
+ = Yes
- = No
.. = No data available
# = Unclear
(Canada)= The instrument will be in operation in Canada on or before 1-1-1993.

Incentive effects:

With the Canadian charge an incentive effect is conceivable as permits are revised if applicants demonstrate that actual emissions are below permitted emissions. There is as yet no data on actual incentive effects.

In Japan ambient concentration levels of SO_2 have been reduced substantially, but it is unclear to what extent this is due to the charge.

The incentive effect of the Swedish NO_x charge has surpassed expectations. The charge speeded up compliance to sharper emission standards to be imposed in 1995. The US air pollution permit fees, to be imposed from January 1st 1993 on, can have incentive effects in cases where control costs are very low.

The Swedish NO_x-charge is levied on actual emissions of heat and power producers with a capacity of over 10 MW and production exceeding 50 GwH. Smaller installations are not subject to the charge as the fixed cost of metering would be excessive. Only final energy producers are charged, with industrial process burning excluded. The installations subject to the charge emit around 6.5 per cent of total Swedish NO_x emissions.

If emissions are not actually measured standard emission rates (of 600 mg NO_x/MJ for gas turbines and 250 mg NO_x/MJ for other installations) apply. These rates exceed average actual emissions encouraging installation of measurement equipment.

The charge is applied alongside permits. The purpose is to speed up compliance to new emission guidelines, to be imposed in 1995.

All charge revenues are rebated to installations subject to the charge, on the basis of their final energy production. Thus the final revenue impact is zero, but with a redistribution between high emitting and low emitting plants. Rebates are given in the same year as charges are levied.

In 1992 the actual emission reduction has been between 30 and 40 per cent, exceeding the expected emission reduction of 20-25 per cent.

3.2.2   Aircraft noise

In some countries landing fees are differentiated according to noise classes of aircraft, or according to weight or type of aircraft.

In Germany landing fees for aircraft satisfying noise standards specified in ICAO Annex 16, Ch. 3, are considerably lower than for Ch. 2 type aircraft. The Norwegian charge (levied on Bodo and Fornebu airports) is a tax differentiation with zero net revenue.

At German airports the percentage of aircraft satisfying the Ch. 3 standards has increased from 26 per cent in 1987 to 30 per cent in 1988 and 43 per cent in 1989. Whether this is due to the charge is difficult to establish. The Norwegian charge is intended as an incentive charge, but it has not been evaluated.

Table 3.2 **Aircraft noise charges**

Country	charge base	Incentive		Revenue spending
		Int	**Act**	
Belgium	type of aircraft, time of day	-	..	Noise abatement
(France)	Noise characteristics	-	..	Noise abatement
Germany	Noise class of aircraft	+	#	Noise abatement
Japan	Weight and noise level of aircraft	-	..	General budget
Netherlands	Weight and type of aircraft	-	..	Noise abatement
Norway	Noise characteristics	+	..	No net revenue
Portugal	Weight of aircraft	-	..	General budget
Switzerland	Noise characteristics (Classes I-V)	-	..	Noise abatement

Incentive effects:

Most charges are intended to raise revenue for noise abatement, by home insulation, etc.

3.2.3 *Soil protection*

Table 3.3 **Soil protection charges**

Country	Charge base	Incentive		Revenue spending
		Int	**Act**	
Belgium	P and N in manure: number of livestock	-	..	Manure policy
Netherlands	P in manure: number of livestock	+	..	Manure policy
USA_{reg}	Cost sharing for soil improvement	+	..	Soil improvement

Belgium (Flanders) and the Netherlands levy so-called "surplus manure" charges, levied on emissions of Phosphorus (P) and/or Nitrogen (N) in excess of environmentally acceptable maximum manure loads per hectare.

Incentive effects:

The Belgian and Dutch surplus manure charges are redistributive charges, financing manure policy (manure transport, storage and processing).

For the US charge there are no data on incentive effects.

3.2.4   Waste

Below three types of waste charges are distinguished:

-- Municipal waste user charges, raising revenue for waste collection and disposal (3.2.4.1). Municipal waste user charges are a payment for a service.

-- Waste disposal taxes, with fiscal or para fiscal characteristics (3.2.4.2). Waste disposal taxes are distinct from user charges (3.2.4.1) as they are not a payment for a service. Revenue is for the general budget, or is earmarked for a broad range of environmental expenditures such as subsidies on waste treatment and recycling.

-- Hazardous waste charges, raising revenue for hazardous waste processing (3.2.4.3).

3.2.4.1 Municipal waste user charges

Data on municipal waste user charges are incomplete on the following points:

• Private sector involvement. It is unclear to what extent waste collection from firms is privatized. Presumably it is to a considerable extent.

• Degree of cost coverage. User charge revenues may not fully cover costs.

• Percentage of municipalities actually levying the charge.

In table 3.4 the column "Incentive " is omitted as little data are available.

In Finland waste collection is privatized in some municipalities for both households and firms. In the UK waste collection and disposal are financed from local taxes.

Table 3.4 **Municipal waste user charges**

Country	Charge base and rate		Revenue spending
Australia	Households	: FR(AM)	Di
	Firms	: FR(AM)	
Austria	..		..
Belgium	Households	: FR (AM)	Co
	Firms	: ..	
Canada	Households	: FR	Co + Di
		: AM	
Denmark	Households	: FR (AM)	Co + Di
		: AM	
Finland	Households	: AM	Co + Di
	Firms	: AM	
France	Households	: FR (AM)	..
	Firms	: ..	
Germany	Households	: FR	Co + Di
	Firms	: AM	
Iceland	Households	: FR,ECU 8-65/an	Co + Di
	Firms		
Ireland	..		..
Italy	Households	: FR	..
	Firms	: ..	
Japan	Households	: FR (AM)	Co + Di
	Firms	: ..	
Netherlands	Households	: FR (AM)	Co + Di
	Firms	: ..	
Norway	Households	: FR, ECU 44-219/year	Co + Di
	Firms	: AM, ECU 11-44/ton	
Spain	Households	: FR	Co + Di
	Firms	: FR	
Sweden	Households	: FR, ECU 107/year	Co + Di
	Firms	: FR(AM)	
Switzerland	Households	: FR (AM)	Co + Di
	Firms	: FR (AM)	
UK	Households	: -	Co + Di
	Firms	: AM	
USA	Households	: FR (AM)	Co + Di
	Firms	: ..	

Notes :   Key to symbols:
FR   = Flat rate (in some countries rates depend on size of dwelling or household)
AM = Actual measurement
FR(AM)= FR in most municipalities, AM in some
Co   = Collection
Di   = Disposal

Incentive effects:

Charges for households are generally at flat rates, independent of waste supplied. In eight countries municipalities experiment with charges related to actual quantity of waste supplied (weight or volume). Some countries report actual incentive effects. In most countries charges for firms are based on the quantity of waste actually delivered. No data are available on actual incentive effects. From the data it is unclear to what extent waste collection from firms is privatized.

3.2.4.2 Taxes on waste disposal

Taxes on waste disposal are levied on waste supplied to processors such as landfills and incinerators.

Table 3.5 **Taxes on waste disposal**

Country	Tax rate	Incentive		Revenue spending
		Int	Act	
Australia$_{reg}$	ECU 1.4/ton	+	#/+	General budget
Austria	ECU 2.4/ton	−	..	Treatment and recycling
Belgium (Fla)	ECU 3.1-18.9/ton	+	..	Environmental expenditure
(Wal)	..	..	..	
Denmark	ECU 14.4/ton	+	#/+	General budget
France	ECU 2.5/ton	#	..	Treatment and recycling
Germany$_{reg}$	..		..	..
Italy	..		..	..
(Netherlands)	ECU 6.2/ton	#	..	General budget

The Austrian charge is to be raised to ECU 6.7/ton in 1993 and ECU 12.3/ton in 1994.

Rates of the Belgian waste tax depend on type of treatment and waste origin. Revenue is for a fund financing a broad range of environmental projects.

The proposed Dutch waste charge applies to landfills only.

Incentive effects:

In Australia the province of New South Wales reports increased recycling rates due to the charge. For the Belgian tax (Flanders) an incentive effect is officially presumed, but no evaluation has taken place yet.

The Danish waste tax may have had incentive effects, but this is hard to establish due to the simultaneous effects of accompanying waste policies and underlying economic and technological developments.

The Danish Waste Tax

The Danish waste tax was introduced in 1987. It is levied on the weight of waste supplied to landfills and waste incinerators, excluding waste streams for which specific regulations apply. Waste abducted from landfills and incinerators is subtracted from the charge base. All waste processors are required to satisfy specific administrative conditions, such as the presence of adequate weighing apparatus. A side-effect of the tax has been that a number of (difficult to monitor) small processors have had to close down as they were unable to satisfy the administrative requirements.

As the tax is based on weight the effect is mainly on weighty bulk streams, such as building waste.

There is evidence of incentive effects:

- from 1987 to 1989 total registered waste supply decreased by 12 per cent and waste abducted increased by 7 per cent;
- from 1990 on, when the definition of waste was extended, the increase in waste subject to the charge was below expectations.

To what extent the decreasing tendency in waste supply is due to the waste tax is hard to tell, as it is difficult to separate the effect of the tax from other factors, such as the increase in user charges, regulations on waste removal and processing, and autonomous economic and technical developments.

A minor increase in illegal dumping has been reported.

As an unintentional side effect there has been an excessive use of building waste as filling material for road making, noise abatement and the like. Also, as re-usable materials are increasingly being sorted out, waste streams left for disposal are getting more polluted.

For 1993 an increase of the charge rate from ECU 14.4 to ECU 21.6 and ECU 17.73 is envisaged for waste delivered at dumping sites and incinerated waste respectively.

3.2.4.3 *Charges on hazardous waste*

Table 3.6 **Charges on hazardous waste**

Country	Charge base and rate	Incentive		Revenue spending
		Int	Act	
Australia_reg	..	+	..	Collection and processing
Austria	ECU 12/ton	..	..	Clean-up of contaminated sites
Belgium (FI)	ECU 8-63/ton	..	..	Environmental expenditure
Finland	ECU 270/ton on average	#	..	Waste processing
(Portugal)	..	..	..	Waste processing
USA	..	-	-	Clean up of contaminated sites

Notes : Key to symbols:
FR   = Flat rate (in some countries rates depend on size of dwelling or household)
AM = Actual measurement
FR(AM)= FR in most municipalities, AM in some
Co   = Collection
Di   = Disposal

Incentive effects:

Presumably actual rates are too low for incentive effects, but no evaluations have taken place yet.

3.2.5 *Charges on emissions to surface water*

Two types of charges are distinguished:

-- User charges for sewerage and sewage treatment (3.2.5.1). These charges are a payment for the service of providing sewerage and sewage treatment.
-- Waste water effluent charges (3.2.5.2). These charges, on direct discharges only, are levied on all waste water effluent, regardless of actual treatment.

3.2.5.1 *User charges for sewerage and sewage treatment*

As a rule both sewerage systems and sewage treatment plants are operated by municipalities. The exceptions are Belgium, the Netherlands and some municipalities in Germany, where sewage treatment is in the hands of separate water authorities.

Households and firms pay user charges for sewerage and sewage treatment, usually on the basis of water usage. The charge is usually included in water bills.

In most countries industry is metered. In some countries firms pay a charge based on pollution load, or "excess pollution load" - pollution load exceeding pre specified minimum standards.

It is not known to what extent charges cover cost. Municipalities may finance the cost of sewerage and sewage treatment partly out of their general budget.

In table 3.7 the column "Incentives" is omitted as too little data are available.

Incentive effects:

Charges based on actual measurement may have incentive effects. In most countries charges are based on water usage. Therefore any effect on emissions of waste water would be indirect, through reduced water consumption.

In some countries rates for firms are based on pollution load. As to actual incentive effects, little data are available. One regional Australian water board reports incentive effects for major industrial users. Finland reports reduced water usage after introduction of the waste water charge.

The Sydney Water Board

In Australia the Sydney Water Board (SWB) and the Hunter Water Corporation (HWC) levy a charge with a fixed and a variable component. The SWB reports incentive effects for major industrial users. HWC reports reduced water usage.

SWB's administrative costs are 18 per cent of charge revenue. The Board intends to raise the variable component, if distributional problems (especially for large households) can be dealt with satisfactorily. Also the Board wants to extend metering, but this may not be practically feasible for some groups of customers.

Table 3.7 User charges for sewerage and sewage treatment

Country	Charge	Method of measurement
Australia	H: Water usage F: Water usage, pollution load$_{reg}$	FR/AM
Belgium	H: Water usage F: ..	FR/AM ..
Canada	H: Water usage F: Water usage, pollution load$_{reg}$	FR/AM FR/AM
Denmark	H: Water usage F: Water usage, excess pollution load	FR AM
Finland	H: Water usage F: Water usage, excess pollution load	FR/AM AM
France	H: Water usage F: Water usage	.. ..
Germany	H: Water usage F: Water usage, pollution load$_{reg}$	.. FR/AM
Ireland	..	..
Italy	H: Water usage F: ..	.. ..
Netherlands	H: flat rate F: ..	FR ..
New Zealand	..	..
Norway	H: Water usage F: Water usage, excess pollution load	FR FR/AM
Portugal	H: Water usage F: Water usage	FR FR
Spain	H: Water usage F: Water usage	AM AM
Sweden	H: Water usage, F: Water usage, excess pollution load	FR/AM AM
Switzerland	H: Water usage F: Water usage	FR/AM FR/AM
UK	H: Water usage; F/ Water usage, pollution load	FR/AM FR/AM
USA	H: Water usage F: Water usage, pollution load	.. FR/AM

Notes :   Key to symbols :
   H   = Households
   F   = Firms
   FR = Flat rate
   AM = Actual measurement
   FR(AM) = Both FR and AM occur

3.2.5.2 Waste water effluent charges

Table 3.8 Water effluent charges

Country	Charge base	Incentive		Measurement method
		Int	**Act**	
Australia$_{reg}$	F: Pollution load acc. to permit	+	#	AM
Belgium (Fla)	F: Pollution load	+	#	AM
(Wal)	F: Pollution load	..	..	FR/AM
Canada	F: Pollution load	+	#	AM
France	F: Pollution load	#	..	AM
Germany	F: Pollution load related to discharge standard	+	#	AM
(Netherlands)	F: Pollution load	#	+	AM
Portugal	H: Pollution load	..	..	FR
	F: pollution load	..	..	
Spain	F: Pollution load acc. to permit	..	..	AM
USA$_{reg}$	F: Pollution load	..	..	..

Notes : Key to symbols:
H   = Households
F   = Firms
FR = Flat rate
AM = Actual measurement
FR/AM = Both FR and AM occur

Effluent charges are levied on households and firms, independent of actual waste water treatment. Only charges levied on direct discharges are included in table 3.8. Charges on indirect discharges are reported in the previous section.

In all countries revenue is spent on water quality policy and/or subsidies to firms for pollution abatement.

In the Australian province South Australia the effluent charge is based on emissions allowed in licences. The Hunter Water Corporation levies a charge on emissions of small businesses.

In Canada the provinces of British Columbia and Quebec levy a charge based on pollution load, rates varying by degree of toxicity of pollutants.

With the Belgian charge (Flanders) pollution load is measured in pollution equivalents (BOD, COD, suspended materials, nutrient load and heavy metals). The Wallonian charge is comparable in design.

The French charge is implemented by the "Agences de l'Eau". For firms emitting more than 200 "inhabitant equivalents" (a standardized menu of COD, suspended matter, nitrogen, phosphates, toxic materials and dissolved salts) the "Agences" estimate actual emissions. Firms can lower their charge bill if they can prove that actual emissions are below estimates made by the Agence.

Incentive effects:

The Belgian charge has been instituted recently and has not been evaluated yet. The Canadian province of Alberta reports incentive effects. According to two academic dissertations, the Dutch water pollution charge has had incentive effects. In France the waste water effluent charge, is redistributive. In Germany the waste water charge has contributed to an improvement in water quality. Rates are not sufficient for incentive effects, but this may change as rates are to be increased by 170-360 per cent to finance increasing water quality expenditure. The Spanish charge is modeled on the French system. It has no incentive purpose.

The German Water Effluent Charge

The German water effluent charge, originally introduced in 1976 (and adapted afterwards), primarily promotes compliance to permit standard.

The charge is implemented by the States. The charge base is a menu of polluting substances, COD and heavy metals. The charge rate is diminished by 75 per cent if a source can demonstrate compliance standards that are regularly updated according to technological progress. Whenever there is an update, the new standards become, for existing plants, obligatory only after a transitional period. If, however, these plants comply with the new standards before they are obliged to do so, they get the 75 per cent reduction.

The environmental impact of the charge is difficult to assess as it is closely related to the accompanying permit policies.

There are indications of an "announcement effect", as there has been a steep increase in abatement investments in the years immediately preceding the introduction of the charge.

The Dutch Water Pollution Charge

The rate of the Dutch water pollution charge is determined by revenue required for sewage treatment and policies for maintaining and improving water quality generally.

The charge is implemented by the "Water Boards", self governing bodies of surface water users in charge of quantitative and qualitative water management. The charge base is BOD and (in most cases) heavy metals. The charge is levied on all direct and indirect discharges.

Households and small firms pay a fixed amount. According to two academic dissertations [Bressers (1983) and Schuurman (1988)] there has been an incentive effect for large firms that are actually metered.

3.3 Charges on Products

Product charges are levied on:

-- product(s), *e.g.*, batteries
-- product characteristics, *e.g.*, carbon or sulphur content.

The so-called "tax differentiations", such as those on leaded and unleaded car petrol, are included in this category. Tax differentiations all happen to be in the motorcar transport area.

Section 3.3.1 reports on charges in the area of motorcar transport.

Section 3.3.2 groups environmental charges on fossil fuels.

Section 3.3.3 is on environmental charges in agriculture.

Sections 3.3.4 to 3.3.6 report charges on specific products, namely, batteries, lubricant oil and ozone depleting substances.

Section 3.3.7 surveys charges on packaging.

3.3.1   Charges in motorcar transport

3.3.1.1 Car sales tax differentiation

Table 3.9 lists car sales tax differentials between cars with high and low emissions.

Table 3.9 **Car sales tax differentials**

Country	Tax base and rate
Belgium	Cars not satisfying emission standards: ECU 314-419
Canada	Automobile weight: ECU 17-34
Canada$_{reg}$	Fuel efficiency: ECU 340-1985
Finland	Cars not equipped with catalytic converter: ECU 714
Germany	Cars not equipped with catalytic converter: ECU 238-478
Greece	Degree of compliance with emission standards
Japan	Tax deductions for cars with low emissions, electric cars and cars on alternative fuels
Netherlands	Cars not satisfying US-or EC-emission standards: ECU 301-603
Norway	Cars not equipped with catalytic converter: ECU 774
Sweden	Degree of compliance with emission standards: -/-ECU 474-ECU 237
USA	Cars with fuel efficiency below 22.5 miles/gallon ECU 655-4587

The Dutch tax is to be designed differently as of 1-1-1993, since by that date all new cars will have to satisfy EC-standards.

Germany scraps the tax differential on 1-1-1993 for this reason.

Incentive effects:

Greece reports a "complete change" in the market for new cars. All new cars are equipped with catalytic converters. This is due also to the combined application of the tax differentiation with a scrapping refund. The scrapping refund is received only if a new car is bought that is equipped with a catalytic converter.

In many countries there are regulations specifying that catalytic converters will be compulsory at some future date. The tax differentiation has been intended to speed up the market penetration of cars equipped with catalytic converters.

3.3.1.2 Differentiation of annual vehicle tax

In Table 3.10 the tax rate is the differential between cars with high and low emissions.

Table 3.10

Country	Tax base	tax rate
Austria	Equipment with catalytic converter	Dependent on weight class
Denmark	Equipment with catalytic converter	..
Germany	Cylinder capacity and emissions	ECU 3.6/100cc
(Netherlands)	Emissions	..

In Austria there are weight classes determining the applicable tax rate. Cars not equipped with a catalytic converter are classified in the next higher weight class.

The Danish system is to be abolished from 1993 on.

For new cars the German system is to be reformed, with vehicle tax rates dependent on an emission index of major pollutants (hydrocarbons, carbon monoxide, nitrogen dioxide).

Incentive effects: No data are available on incentive effects.

3.3.1.3 Leaded car petrol

All OECD-countries levy excises on car petrol. In some countries a surtax on leaded petrol is part of the car petrol excise. The tax rate indicated below is the difference in tax rates on leaded and unleaded petrol.

The column "incentive effects" provides data about market shares of unleaded.

Table 3.11 Tax differentiation between leaded and unleaded petrol

Country	Tax rate	Incentive effects
Austria	ECU 0.03/l	..
Belgium	ECU 0.03/l	Market share from 0 to 32.5% in 1989-1990
Canada	ECU 0.01/l	Leaded phased out since December 1990
Denmark	ECU 0.07/l	Market share is 75%
Finland	ECU 0.07/l	Market share attained 70% in 1992
France	ECU 0.06/l	Market share rose to 25% in 1991
Germany	ECU 0.04/l	Market share from 11% to 88% in 1986-1992
Iceland	ECU 0.02/l	Market share exceeds 70%
Ireland	..	..
Netherlands	ECU 0.05/l	Market share from 32 to 75% in 1989-1992
New Zealand	..	..
Norway	ECU 0.07/l	Market share from 17% to 55%
Portugal	ECU 0.05/l	..
Sweden	ECU 0.04/l	Market share attained 55% in 1991
Switzerland	ECU 0.04/l	Market share attained 65% in 1992
UK	..	..

Notes : Revenue is for the general budget, except in Iceland where it is earmarked for road construction and maintenance.

Incentive effects:

Market shares of unleaded petrol have risen, but it is unclear to what extent this is due to the tax differential or to the increasing number of cars equipped with catalytic converters and pending regulation on this issue.

A practical difficulty is to keep the tax differential tuned to the changing market price differential between leaded and unleaded petrol. As market prices of unleaded have been progressively falling since the institution of the tax differential, in most countries unleaded is now cheaper than leaded.

In Spain there is no tax differentiation, but the market price of unleaded is lower than leaded.

3.3.2   *Charges on fossil fuels*

3.3.2.1   *Carbon taxes*

Carbon taxes are levied on top of existing excises on fossil fuels. Table 3.12 provides the rates of explicit carbon taxes, and also the carbon tax rates implicit in existing excises (*cf.* Hoeller and Coppel (1992)].

Most countries levying carbon taxes differentiate rates per sector. The indicated charge rates are the general rates.

In Denmark the tax rate is ECU 11.1 for households and non-VAT registered companies and ECU 5.5 for non-VAT registered companies. In Norway only coal and coke used for energy purposes is taxed. Production of cement is exempted. Fuel used in coastal fisheries is exempted. Oil used in the pulp and paper industry and in greenhouses is levied at half of the CO_2 tax. In the Netherlands feedstocks are excluded. In Sweden the tax rate for industry and horticulture is now at ECU 9.5/ton CO_2.

Finland will double the tax rate on 1-1-1993. The Italian proposal is only for fuels utilized in production of thermal energy in installations covered by the EC-directive on Large Combustion Plants. The Dutch charge rate rises to ECU 1.6 on 1-7-1992.

Table 3.12   **Explicit and implicit carbon taxes**

Country	Rate per ton CO_2	Implicit rate of existing excises	Incentive	
			Int	Act
Denmark	ECU 5.5-11.1	ECU 26.3	+	..
Finland	ECU 1.1	ECU 19.1	#	..
(Italy)	ECU 1.7	ECU 39.9	..	..
Netherlands	ECU 0.4	ECU 15.9	-	..
Norway	ECU 13.8 on coal and coke ECU 15.7 on fuel oils ECU 40.6 on gasoline ECU 40.6 on natural gas	ECU 32.5	+	..
Sweden	ECU 37.9	ECU 38.2	+	#

Incentive effects:

Charges in Finland and the Netherlands are too low for incentive effects. In Denmark, Norway and Sweden the carbon charges have only recently been instituted.

In evaluating incentive effects, the impacts of differences between countries in existing excises on fossil fuels should not be lost sight of. In Sweden, energy and CO_2 taxation is so high that some district heating plants are changing from fossil fuels to bio fuels.

Table 3.13 **Charges on sulphur content of fuels**

Country	Charge base	Incentive		Revenue spending
		Int	Act	
Norway	S-weight % of oil	+	#	General budget
Sweden	S-weight % of oil, coal and peat	+	+	General budget

The Norwegian charge is levied per 0.025 S-weight percentage at a rate of ECU 0.008/lr. It is not levied on oil with sulphur content lower than 0.05 per cent.

The Swedish charge is levied per 0.1 per cent S-weight at a rate of ECU 3.2 per m^3 of diesel fuel and heating oil, exceeding a threshold of 0.1 per cent S-content. It is ECU 3.6/kg for coal, coke and peat. The charge approximates an emission charge as it is repayable if a taxpayer can demonstrate an actual reduction of SO$_x$ emissions.

On 1-7-1993 Finland will impose a tax differentiation of ECU 0.024/lr between standard quality and sulphur free diesel oil (S-content below 0.005 weight percentage).

The Swedish Sulphur Tax

A recent official evaluation indicates that in Sweden sulphur content of oil has decreased by around 30 per cent between 1990 and 1992 as a result of the tax. Emissions from burning coal and peat have also decreased considerably. The tax has made it profitable to clean flue gases to a larger degree than before. Preliminary tax figures for 1992 reveal an increased reduction of sulphur emissions.

Administrative costs are probably less than 1 per cent of revenue.

Repayments of the tax, if actual reductions of SO2-emissions are demonstrated, occurs on a rather large scale. Emissions are reduced not only by more intensive use of flue gas cleaning, but also by substituting fossil fuels. The CO$_2$ tax also provides an additional incentive.

Incentive effects:

Both the Norwegian and the Swedish sulphur taxes are intended as incentive charges. Presumably both have had incentive effects, especially the Swedish charge in view of the unexpected revenue shortfall.

As there are accompanying regulatory and charging policies the effect of the sulphur charges is difficult to isolate.

3.3.3 Charges in agriculture

3.3.3.1 Fertilizer charges

Table 3.14 **Charges on fertilizers**

Country	Charge base, rate and percentage of price	Incentive		Revenue spending
		Int	Act	
Austria	N-, P- and K- content: ECU 0.31, ECU 0.18, and ECU 0.09 per kg.	-	-	Subsidies, environmental expenditure
Finland	N- and P- content: ECU 0.41 and 0.27/kg. (5-20% of price).	+	#	Agricultural subsidies, general budget
Norway	N- and P- content: ECU 0.13 (19% of price) and ECU 0.24/kg. (11% of price)	+	#	General budget
Sweden	N- and P- content, ECU 0.07 and 0.14/kg. (10% of price).	+	+	Subsidies, environmental expenditure
USA$_{rég}$	ECU 0.07-1.11/ton (<=2.5% of price)	..	..	Environmental expenditure

In Finland there has been a decrease in the use of Phosphorus, but this may be due to other policy instruments as well. The Finnish charge, with a higher rate for Nitrogen, is not primarily based on environmental considerations. Between 1980 and 1988 Phosphorus usage per hectare in Norway decreased by around 40 per cent, remaining constant thereafter.

Until recently in Sweden a price regulation charge of about 20 per cent of price was applied next to the environmental charge.

Incentive effects:

The Swedish Board of Agriculture calculated that the optimum input level of Nitrogen fertilizer falls by 10-15 per cent at the prevailing 30 per cent charge rate (the environmental charge plus the price regulation charge). In real life the use of nitrogen has fallen less.

Table 3.15 **Charges on pesticides**

Country	Charge base and rate	Incentive Int	Act	Revenue spending
Norway	13% on wholesale price	+	..	General budget
Sweden	ECU 0.9/kg active ingredient ECU 3.6 per treated hectare	+	#	Environmental expenditure

The Swedish charge is levied on active ingredients and is about 5 per cent of price. From 1986 to 1992 there was also a "price regulation charge" on pesticides, of between ECU 3.6 and ECU 4.6 per dose and per hectare, amounting to 20 per cent of pesticides' price. Costs of administration are low.

Incentive effects: The Swedish Board of Agriculture estimates the price elasticity of pesticides, on the basis of empirical data, at 0.2-0.5

3.3.4 *Batteries*

In Sweden the charge is levied only if HgO_x and Cd content together exceed 0.25 per cent of weight.

Incentive effects: The charges are for financing only. No incentive effects are intended.

Table 3.16 **Charges on batteries**

Country	Charge base and rate	Incentive Int	Act	Revenue spending
Canada_reg	Lead-acid batteries > 2 kg: ECU 2.8/kg.	-	-	Recycling, environmental expenditure
Denmark	NiCd-batteries: ECU 0.2/piece Battery packages: ECU 0.9/piece	-	-	Collection, treatment and recycling
Portugal	Lead batteries: ECU 1-5/piece	-	-	Collection, treatment and recycling
Sweden	Lead batteries > 3 kg: ECU 3.8/kg HgO_x batteries: ECU 2.7/kg NiCd batteries: ECU 1.5/kg	-	-	Collection, treatment and recycling

3.3.5   Lubricant oil

Table 3.17 **Charges on lubricant oil**

Country	Rate	Incentive Int	Act	Revenue spending
Finland	ECU 0.04/kg	-	-	Waste oil treatment
France	ECU 0.009/lr	-	-	Waste oil treatment
Italy	ECU 0.003/lr	-	-	Waste oil treatment
Norway	ECU 0.055/lr	-	-	General budget
USA$_{reg}$	..	-	-	Waste oil treatment

The rate of the Italian charge applies as of 1-1-1987.

The Norwegian charge will be amended if the oil industry establishes an environmentally acceptable system for the collection and treatment of waste oils.

Incentive effects:

In all countries the charge is too low for incentive effects. Lubricant oil charges are intended as revenue raising instruments to finance waste oil treatment.

3.3.6   Ozone depleting chemicals

Table 3.18 **Charges on ozone depleting chemicals**

Country	Charge base and rate	Incentive Int	Act	Revenue spending
Australia	CFC's: ECU 0.07/kg	-	-	CFC phase out
(Austria)	Appliances containing refrigerants	-	-	Environmental expenditure
Denmark	CFC's and Halons: ECU 3.3/kg.	#	#	General budget, environmental expenditure
USA	Ozone depleting chemicals: chemicals: ECU 2.0-2.4/kg CFC-11	#	+	General budget

In Australia some provinces have fees on CFC's in addition to the national charge. The Danish and the Australian charge are levied on domestic production and imports. The Danish charge is administered next to a set of regulatory controls. In Denmark CFC-consumption fell by 60 per cent between 1986 and 1991. Whether this is due to the tax or the regulatory program is not known. There have been practical problems in identifying CFC-content of imported products.

The US-charge is levied on all ozone depleting chemicals. The tax for a specific chemical is determined by taking a base amount for the tax and multiplying it by the "ozone-depleting factor" applicable to the particular chemical. The charge rate is ECU 2.0 for chemicals restricted by the Montreal Protocol, and ECU 2.4 for chemicals restricted by the amended Montreal Protocol. The charge is applied next to a system of tradable production quota. It is designed as a windfall-profits tax, skimming off the windfall profits created by production limitations imposed by the tradable quota scheme. It will be raised progressively in the coming years. The charge rate increases over time.

Incentive effects:

According to Oates (1992) the US charge has had incentive effects on the use of CFC's in soft foams. In Denmark and the USA charges are applied next to quantitative controls, impairing the task of separately identifying incentive effects.

3.3.7　Product packaging

Table 3.19　**Charges on packaging**

Country	Charge base and rate	Incentive Int	Act	Revenue spending
(Belgium)	Packaging waste	..	..	..
Canada_reg	Non refillable beverage containers	..	..	Mixed
Denmark	Glass and plastic beverage containers: * ECU 0.06 for 10-60 cl * ECU 0.18 for 60-106 cl * ECU 0.25 for > 106 cl Metal beverage cans: ECU 0.09 Cardboard and laminated beverage packaging: * ECU 0.04 for 10-60 cl * ECU 0.08 for 60-106 cl * ECU 0.21 for > 106 cl Liquid dairy products: ECU 0.01	+	#	General budget
Finland	Disposable beverage containers: * Beer: ECU 0.16/lr (5% of price) * Soft drinks (glass and metal): ECU 0.48/lr (10-50% of price) * Soft drinks (other): ECU 0.32/lr	+	+	General budget
Norway	Non returnable beverage containers: * Beer: ECU 0.27 * Carbonated soft drinks: ECU 0.38 * Non-carbonated beverages: ECU 0.05 * Wine and liquor: ECU 0.27	+	+	General budget
Portugal	Glass beverage containers 33-100 cl: ECU 0.05	..	..	General budget
Sweden	Beverage containers * Returnable glass, aluminium: ECU 0.01 * Disposable containers 20-300 cl: ECU 0.01-0.03	-	-	General budget
USA_reg	Litter generating products	-	-	Waste treatment

The Danish Packaging Charge

The purpose of the Danish packaging charge, levied only on new glass bottles, is to encourage collection and re-use of bottles (*e.g.*, by instituting deposit refund systems). So the rate of the charge must be high enough to cover the costs of collection and cleaning of used bottles. These costs are especially high in cases of "open" recollection, *i.e.*, if producers do not themselves operate recollection activities. Therefore the charge on returnable glass bottles is high, but this impairs the competitive position of glass bottles vis-a-vis non-returnable packaging materials, such as cardboard and laminates.

The charge rate on plastic bottles which is high compared to rates on cardboard and laminates, is not justified by environmental considerations.

A study prepared by the Danish Environmental Protection Agency concluded that packaging charges account only for a minor part of the costs influencing the choice of packaging. If products are distributed in a closed circulation, in which distribution and recollection are operated by the manufacturers, there are optimum conditions for the use of returnable packaging. Generally speaking, the technical, logistical and distributional conditions for the use of returnable packagings must be fulfilled if packaging charges are to have incentive effects.

In Sweden paper and cardboard containers are exempted from the charge. The packaging tax will be removed when producers (as proposed by the Government) take over the responsibility for packaging waste.

Incentive effects:

The evidence on effects of the Danish packaging charge is inconclusive. The charges are only a minor part of the total costs influencing the choice of packaging. There appeared to be a conflict between the need to finance returnable packaging recycling systems, calling for a high charge rate, and the need to maintain the competitive position of returnable packagings vis-a-vis non-returnable packagings.

In Finland the market share of returnable containers has risen to 90 per cent.

In Norway the majority of beverages is sold in returnable containers that are not taxed. A new system is presently under development and may opt for a more extensive differentiation than the present scheme.

In Sweden the charge is too low for incentive effects. The deposit refund systems are considered to be more effective.

3.3.8   Miscellaneous product charges

General excises on motor fuels, with revenue for the general budget, are not included in this survey, as their primary intention is (and always has been) to raise revenue for the general budget.

Table 3.20 Miscellaneous product charges

Country	Description and rate	Incentive Int	Incentive Act	Revenue spending
Austria	Car registration tax dependent on fuel use	+	#	General budget
Canada	Car airconditioners: ECU 57	+	..	General budget
Canada$_{reg}$	Disposable diapers (6-7% of price)	+	..	General budget
Canada$_{reg}$	Car tires: ECU 1.1-2.8	-	..	Mixed
Denmark	Conventional light bulbs: ECU 0.06-1.1	..	..	General budget
	Raw materials: ECU 0.55/ton	#	..	General budget
	Disposable tableware: 1/3 of price (or 50% of import value)	+	..	General budget
	Small chemicals packaging: 1/6 of price	#	..	General budget
(Denmark)	Tax differentiation on diesel oil: ECU 0.01/lr.	..	..	No net revenue
Italy	Plastic shopping bags: ECU 0.06	+	+	General budget
Finland	Oil pollution combatting charge: ECU 0.35-0.70 per ton of crude oil	-	-	Oil spill damage abatement
	Diesel oil tax: ECU 0.04/lr.	+	..	General budget
	Nuclear waste charge	-	-	Nuclear waste processing
(Finland)	Tax differentiation on gasoline: ECU 0.008/lr. (between "standard" and "reformulated" quality)	+	..	General budget
Greece	Transport fuels: ECU 0.02/lr.	-	-	Environmental expend.
Netherlands	Fuel charge: ECU 0.14/GigaJoule	-	-	General budget
Sweden	Charge on domestic aviation: ECU 1.42/kg CH-NO$_x$, ECU 0.09/kg fuel	+	#	General budget
	Tax differentiation on petroleum products: ECU 11-64/m$_3$, dep. on env. characteristics	+	+	No net revenue
	Charge on electricity: ECU 0.002/kwH	-	-	Nuclear waste processing
USA	Car tires (in 27 states): ECU 0.16-0.98	-	-	Recycling
	Chemicals (ECU 0.14-6.64/ton), crude, oil, corporate taxation	-	-	Superfund:cleaning contaminated sites

Revenue of the Austrian car registration tax is used to reduce the VAT rate for new vehicles.

Until 1992 revenue of the Dutch environmental fuel charge was earmarked for environmental expenditure. Now the earmarking has been rescinded and "environmental user charges" on waste (cf. 3.1.4.2) and ground water have been proposed.

Taxes on Plastic Bags in Italy

In Italy consumption of plastic shopping bags has been reduced by 20-30 per cent immediately after introduction of an incentive charge in 1988 (between 1983 and 1988 plastic bag use had increased by 37 per cent).

Revenue fell 85 per cent short of expectations, possibly due to charge evasion by small producers [Malaman and Ranci (1991)].

The charge is not levied on "biodegradable" bags, but an official standard for this is yet to be established. The charge, and the public debate surrounding it, have served to focus consumer attention on economy in use, while producer R&D efforts on biodegradable bags have been stepped up [Malaman and Ranci (1991)].

Incentive effects:

The Italian tax on plastic shopping bags, at 200 per cent of market price, has had incentive effects.

The Swedish charge on domestic aviation is fixed per flight and type of aircraft. The tax has speeded up the introduction of new planes with lower emissions by approximately 1-2 years.

In Sweden diesel oils are classified in three classes on the basis of environmental characteristics (sulphur, aromatics, etc.), with tax rebates of respectively ECU 53 and ECU 30/m$_3$ for class 1 and 2 (environmental diesel). The tax rebates are larger than the extra cost of production. Of all diesel sold 75 per cent is of class 1 or 2 now, compared to 1% two years before. Average sulphur content in diesel oil has fallen to around 0.03 per cent. The cost for government in the form of lost taxes is ECU 70 million.

3.4 Deposit refunds

The (V) or (M) column indicates whether the deposit refund has been instituted voluntarily (for economic reasons) by industry (V) or has been made mandatory (M) by government. Systems based on voluntary agreements of government with industry are indicated by M/V. Historically deposit refunds have been instituted by industry itself, presumably for economic reasons. Recently deposit refund systems have been mandated, or promoted, by governments for environmental reasons.

3.4.1   Car hulks

Table 3.21 **Deposit-refund on car hulks**

Country	Item	(V) or (M)	Deposit	Refund	Return percentage
Greece	Car hulks older than 15 yr.	M	-	-	
Norway	Car hulks, snowmobiles	M	ECU 77	ECU 110	80-90%
Sweden	Functioning cars < 3.5 ton	M	ECU 101	ECU 178	80-90%
	Car hulks < 3.5 ton	M	ECU 101	ECU 59	80-90%

The Greek deposit refund is combined with a tax differentiation. A refund is payable only if a new car is bought that satisfies EC-emission standards.

In Sweden the annual car control must be passed a maximum of 14 months before scrapping, otherwise the refund will be at the low rate (ECU 59). The idea is to make it more attractive to scrap old cars and buy new ones that satisfy higher emission standards. The aim of the low refund (ECU 59) is more modest *i.e.* to avoid littering of car hulks.

Incentive effects: Return percentages are between 80 per cent and 90 per cent.

3.4.2   Metal cans

Table 3.22 **Deposit refund on metal cans**

Country	Item	Rate (perc. of price)	Return percentage
Australia$_{reg}$	Beer cans	ECU 0.02 (4%)	89%
	Soft drink cans	ECU 0.02 (5%)	89%
Canada$_{reg}$	Metal containers	ECU 0.03-0.11	> 40%
Portugal	Beverage containers	..	..
Sweden	Aluminium cans	ECU 0.07	80-90%
USA$_{reg}$	Soft drinks	..	..

Incentive effects: Return percentages vary between 40-50 per cent and around 90 per cent.

83

3.4.3 Plastic beverage containers

Table 3.23 Deposit-refund on plastic beverage containers

Country	Item	(V) or (M)	Rate (% of price)	Return percentage
Australia$_{reg}$	PET-bottles	M	ECU 0.02 (2-4%)	62%
Austria	Plastic reusable containers	M	ECU 0.25 (20%)	60-30%
Canada$_{reg}$	Plastic beverage containers	M	ECU 0.03-0.05	> 60%
Denmark	PET-bottles < 50 cl - > 50 cl	M	ECU 0.20-0.55	80-90%
Finland	PET bottles > 1 lr.	M/V	ECU 0.32 (10-30%)	90-100%
Germany	Non refillable pl. bottles	M/V	ECU 0.22	..
Iceland	Plastic bottles	M	ECU 0.07 (3-10%)	60-80%
Netherlands	PET-bottles	M/V	ECU 0.35 (30-50%)	90-100%
Norway	PET-bottles <1 lr. -> 1 lr.	M	ECU 0.25-0.63	90-100%
Portugal	Plastic reusable containers	V	..	..
Sweden	PET-bottles	M	ECU 0.47 (20%)	90-100%
USA$_{reg}$	Beer and soft drinks	M	..	72-90%

Incentive effects: Return percentages are all over 60%, indicating high effectiveness.

3.4.4 Glass bottles

Table 3.24 **Deposit-refunds on glass bottles**

Country	Type of bottle	(M) or (V)	Rate (% of price)	Return percentage
Australia$_{reg}$	Soft drinks, refillable	V	ECU 0.05-0.10 (10-15%)	84-96%
	Soft drinks, disposable	M	ECU 0.02 (5%)	
Austria	Beer, wine, soft drinks, milk	V	..	..
Belgium	Beer, soft drinks	..	..	..
Canada$_{reg}$	Beer, wine, liquor a.o	M/V	ECU 0.03-0.23	> 60%
Denmark	Beer	V	ECU 0.14 (20-40%)	90-100%
	Wine (recyclable)	V	ECU 0.14 (4%)	40-60%
	Soft drinks	V	ECU 0.14-0.44 (33-50%)	90-100%
Finland	Beer	M/V	ECU 0.08 (5-10%)	90-100%
	Wine, liquor	M/V	ECU 0.08 (0-5%)	60-80%
	Soft drinks	M/V	ECU 0.08-0.32 (10%)	90-100%
	Cases	V	ECU 2.22	..
France	Beer, soft drinks	..	..	..
Germany	Beer	V	ECU 0.07	90-100%
	Soft drinks, wine	V	ECU 0.13	90-100%
Iceland	Alcoholic beverages	M	ECU 0.07 (0.5%)	..
	Mineral water	M	ECU 0.18 (18-20%)	60-80%
Netherlands	Beer (<35-100 cl)	V	ECU 0.05-0.18	99%
	Soft drinks (1.0-1.5 lr)	V	ECU 0.18-0.35 (37-45%)	95-98%
	Milk, dairy products (lr)	V	ECU 0.18 (20-50%)	..
Norway	Beer	M/V	ECU 0.11-0.22 (10%)	90-100%
	Carbonated soft drinks	M/V	ECU 0.11-0.22 (20%)	90-100%
	Wine and liquor	M/V	ECU 0.11-0.22 (<2%)	40-60%
	Cases	M/V	ECU 1.76	..
Portugal	Beer, wine and soft drinks	V	..	..
Sweden	Beer/soft drinks < 1 lr	M/V	ECU 0.07-0.12	90-100%
	Wine and liquor	M/V	ECU 0.24	60-80%
Switzerland	Beverage bottles	M	ECU 0.10-0.26	..
Turkey	Bottles	..	..	..
USA$_{reg}$	Beer, soft drinks	M	..	72-90%

In Finland deposit refund systems approved by the Ministry of the Environment are exempted from the surtax on packaging. This is also valid for plastic beverage containers.

Incentive effects:

With deposit refunds on beer and soft drinks, return percentages are between 90 and 100%. For wine and liquor, return percentages are 40-80%. As a percentage of price deposit refunds on beer and soft drinks are highest.

3.4.5   Miscellaneous deposit refunds

Table 3.25 **Miscellaneous deposit refunds**

Country	Item	(M) or (V)	Rate (% of price)	Return percentage
Austria	Fluorescent light bulbs	M	ECU 0.5	60-80%
(Germany)	Packaging of detergents	M	ECU 0.2-0.4	..
	Packaging of drinks	M	ECU 0.2-0.4	..
	Packag. of dispersion paints	M	ECU 0.9	..
	Beverage containers	M	..	..
USA$_{reg}$	Vehicle batteries	M	..	..

In Germany the deposit refunds will be mandated only if pre specified targets for recollecting, reprocessing or refillables market shares are not attained voluntarily.

Table 3.26 **Tradeable permit systems**

Country	Description
Australia$_{reg}$	Salt reduction credits
Canada	CFC's Acid rain control
Germany	Air pollution: offsets and netting
USA	Production and consumption rights of ozone depleting chemicals Acid Rain Allowance Trading Oxygenated Gasoline Credits Low Emissions Vehicle Credits Emissions Averaging
USA$_{reg}$	Air pollution: Emissions Trading Water Pollution Wetland Mitigation Banking

By 1993 the US had already achieved a 50 per cent reduction in the production and consumption of CFC's. It aims to achieve a 75 per cent reduction by 1994, an 85 per cent reduction by 1995 and a phase out by 1996. It will also achieve a halon phase out by 1994 (all reductions from a 1986 baseline). Production rights have been grandfathered to existing producers on the basis of their 1986 production. Consumption rights have been allocated to producers (as production minus exports) and to importing firms.

Consistent with the Montreal Protocol, producers are allowed to increase their production rights by 10 per cent to meet the basic domestic needs of certain developing countries. This amount will go up to 15 per cent in 1995. Also consistent with the Protocol, production rights can be transferred to producers in signatory countries to the Montreal protocol. Imports from non-signatory countries are forbidden. To skim off producer rents created by the mandated production cutback a charge has been instituted.

The US Acid Rain Program sets as its primary goal the reduction of annual SO_2-emissions by 10 million tons below 1980 levels with a national limit, or cap, of 8.95 million tons by 2010 on utility sources and a cap of 5.6 million tons on industrial sources. The utilities' costs of compliance are reduced through an allowance trading program. Affected utility units are allocated allowances based on their historic fuel consumption, and a restricted emission rate. Each allowance authorizes a unit to emit one ton of SO_2. If a utility reduces its emissions below the number of allowances it holds at the end of the year, it may sell or trade the extra allowances to other utilities whose emission levels exceed their allowance supply, or it may save them for future years. A small portion (2.8 per cent) of the allowances allocated to utilities is set aside for an annual auction and sale program, to provide an early price signal to the market and an additional source of allowances. The proceeds are returned to utilities.

The environmental benefits of the Acid Rain Program are assured through continuous monitoring of SO_2 emissions, using a specified monitoring and quarterly reporting system. Severe monetary and allowance penalties are imposed on violators.

Tradeable Permits in the USA

In the USA tradeable permit systems have been functioning since 1976. Experiences have been extensively documented by EPA and independent researchers [Tietenberg (1985), Hahn (1989), Kete (1991), U.S. EPA (1992))]

Emissions Trading, the first major U.S. application involving tradeable permits, is superimposed on a program of direct regulation that remains the nucleus of air quality policy. The Emissions Trading Policy, issued in 1982 and revised in 1986, allows the trading of Emission Reduction Credits (ERC's), which are surplus emission reductions achieved beyond baseline emission levels. ERC's can be used for "bubbles", giving sources flexibility in satisfying regulatory standards that have been defined on an emission point basis. "Offsets" enable major new sources to locate in areas where ambient quality is below federal standards, on condition that they satisfy the strictest standards themselves and compensate for their new emissions by obtaining ERC's from other sources in the area. "Netting" exempts modifications of major existing sources from certain new source requirements, so long as no significant net increase in emissions occurs within a facility. "Banking" enables sources to store ERC's for future use.

The offset and netting programs have been extensively utilized. The extent of trading under the limited program has been limited so far, with virtually all trades intra-plant. This is due largely to a problem of timing. The release of the revised Emissions Trading Policy in December 1986 came too late with respect to pre-established (1987 or earlier) industry compliance deadlines. Limited use of the bubble program is also explained by the program's restricted scope and the complexity created by grafting a market-based approach onto an existing command-and-control framework [Hahn and Hester (1989), Merrifield (1990)]. Nevertheless, some significant savings have occurred.

The use of bubbles and other forms of emissions trading will increase substantially under the 1990 amendments to the Clean Air Act. Many States and local areas are already developing or exploring trading programs to meet new air quality mandates. In February 1993, EPA issued proposed Economic Incentive Program Rules which will expand upon the previous options for emissions trading.

Credits for the Oxygenated Gasoline Program can be earned by refiners, blenders and importers for having a greater than required oxygen content in their gasoline and these credits can be transferred to refiners or importers with gasoline too low in oxygen content.

In the Low Emission Vehicle Credit Program tradeable credits can be obtained by manufacturers who sell more clean-fuel vehicles than required.

Emissions Averaging is a trading program where all trades are internal to a plant or firm. Emissions averaging is allowed to meet industry-specific Reasonably Available Control technology (RACT) standards. It is used to control motor vehicle pollution from heavy duty truck engines in a fleet. Also, it is included in California's program for reformulating gasoline and over time, is a part of the Hazardous Air Pollutant Early Reduction Program.

Tradeable water pollution rights are implemented in the States of Colorado (Dillon Reservoir and Cherry Creek Reservoir), Wisconsin (Fox River) and North Carolina (Tar-Pimlico Basin).

Ten states have a program for Wetland Mitigation Banking. A mitigation bank can involve the enhancement of an already deteriorated wetland area or the creation of new wetlands through the diversion of water into an upland area. Mitigation credits (usually defined in terms of habitat units or acres) are earned by the bank and available for sale to developers to meet state-imposed mitigation requirements.

The Australian states of New South Wales, Victoria, and South Australia participate in the Murray Darling Basin Salinity and Drainage strategy, executed by the Murray-Darling Basin Commission. The system works when investments in capital works to manage salt entering the river system and better overall river management generates "salt credits". Credits are transferable between states, but are generally applied in the state to offset debits from drainage water entering the river system. Credits are not tradeable between industries and individuals, but is possible that the system will be revised in this direction.

Canada does not have a formal tradeable permit system, but the acid rain and CFC control programs contain elements of it. Ontario Hydro, the province of Ontario's electric utility, is free to shift or "trade" emissions between its electricity generating stations. Also the Province of Ontario implicitly allows trading between SO_2 and NO_x emissions.

Producers of CFC's are allowed to substitute production between facilities (internal trading). The legislation also allows trading, within firms, between the five types of CFCs subject to the legislation.

In Germany offsets are allowed in air pollution for substances subject to the "TA Luft". New plants can settle in a region that surpasses ambient standards set in the TA Luft, on the condition that emission control measures on existing emission units in the region are implemented reducing ambient air quality, including the emissions of the new plant, below the ex-ante level whereby the ambient standards must not be surpassed by more than 1 per cent. For existing plants, that are required to conform to the most recent emission standards, exceptions to this requirement can be granted in a similar fashion (comparable to the "netting" provision in US Emissions Trading programmes).

3.5.1 *Trading activity and cost savings*

Table 3.27 provides an estimate of the impacts of the Emissions Trading Program up to 1986.

Table 3.27 **Results of the US emission trading program**

Activity	Internal transactions (estimate)	External transactions (estimate)	Cost savings (mln. dollars)
Netting	5000-12000	Not allowed	$25-300 in permitting costs $500-12000 in emission control
Offsets	1800	200	no estimate available
Bubbles	129	2	$ 435
Banking	< 100	< 20	Small

Source: Hahn and Hester [1989]

The offsets and netting provisions in German air pollution regulation are rarely used for a number of reasons, namely, the areas over which the emissions can be substituted are rather small, substitution between substances is not allowed and emission savings are not formally tradeable impairing the possibility of involving different firms. Also, in many cases, abatement cost curves show increasing returns to scale and indivisibilities, actually leaving sources little freedom to choose emission levels. Potential trades among firms are small when they all face the same small number of abatement options [Klepper (1992)].

3.6 Enforcement Incentives

This paragraph lists non-compliance fees and performance bonds. Only non-compliance fees that are proportional to the degree of non-compliance, or to damage inflicted, are included.

The Swedish oil discharge fee (ECU 700 on average) is too low for incentive effects. With the environmental protection charge that can be levied on all violations of environmental regulations, it has appeared to be troublesome to demonstrate in court the extent of non-compliance benefits reaped. In 11 years there have been 9 cases only, with a charge imposed in 4 cases.

In the US $100 million in damages have been paid until 1986 in the framework of the liability for release of hazardous waste. For the non-conformance penalty on heavy vehicles $ 10 million in penalties have been paid in 1987-1989.

The non-compliance fee for SO_2-emissions, to be instituted on 1-1-1993, is a complement to the scheme of tradeable allowances that has been instituted for 1993 and later in the revised Clean Air Act for acid rain control. The fee is approximately 300 per cent of the expected market price for allowances.

Table 3.28 Enforcement incentives

Country	Description	Proportional to
Australia$_{reg}$	Performance bonds on obligation to rehabilitate landscape after mining Performance bonds on feedlots and marine environment protection	Expected cost of rehabilitation Expected damage
Canada	Violations of Environmental Protection	Estimate of monetary benefits
Canada$_{reg}$	Security deposits for resource exploration and land reclamation and land reclamation	Amount of land disturbed and cost of rehabilitation
Sweden	Discharges of oil ships Environmental protection charge	amount of discharge, tonnage Non-compliance benefits
USA	Liability for release of hazardous waste Non conformance penalty for emissions by heavy vehicles and engines	Damage inflicted Degree of non-compliance
(USA)	Acid Rain Control: Emissions of SO_2 in excess of (tradeable) allowances	US$ 2000/ton plus offsets to compensate

Incentive effects:

Rather little data are available. As a general point, it is difficult to establish a benchmark for what count as "incentive effects".

Appendix I: Data Sources

ECOPLAN (1993), Umweltabgaben in Europa, report prepared for the Swiss Ministry of Environment, Forestry and Landscape, Bern 1993.

HAUGLAND, T., LUNDE, A.T and ROLAND, K (1991), "A review and comparison of CO_2-taxes in the Nordic countries", ECON Centre for Economic Analysis, Oslo November.

NORDIC COUNCIL OF MINISTERS (1991), "The Use of Economic Measures in Nordic Environmental Policy", Stockholm, April.

OECD (1991a), "Recent developments in the use of economic instruments for environmental protection in OECD countries", Environment Monograph No 41, Paris, February.

OECD (1993), "Environmental taxes in OECD Countries: A Survey", OECD Environment monographs, No 71, Paris.

OECD (1994), *Environment and taxation: The cases of the Netherlands, Sweden and the United States*, OECD, Paris.

OECD (1994), *Environnement et fiscalité: le cas de la France*, OECD, Paris.

OPSCHOOR, J.B. and VOS, J.B. (1989), *Economic Instruments for Environmental Protection*, OECD Paris.

DE SAVORNIN LOHMAN, A.F. (1991), "Financial Instruments and Economic Incentives in OECD Countries", Paper presented to BCSD-workshop "Economic instruments from the business perspective", London, July 12-14.

UK Department of the Environment (1990), "Market Mechanisms, Charging and Subsidies" (plus Annexes), report prepared by ERL Ltd, London, January.

VOS, J.B. *et al* (1992), "Foreign experiences with financial instruments for environmental policy", DHV/IVM, March.

OECD (1993), "Applying economic instruments to packaging waste: Practical issues for product charges and deposit-refund systems", OECD Environment monograph No. 82, Paris.

Appendix II: Exchange rates against the ECU on 1-1-1992

Rates are expressed in national currency/ECU.

Australian dollar	2.008
Austrian schilling	16.31
Belgian franc	47.72
Canadian dollar	1.763
Danish crown	9.024
Dutch guilder	2.610
Finnish mark	6.307
French franc	7.904
German mark	2.313
Greek drachme	267.5
Iceland crown	84.87
Irish pound	0.872
Italian lire	1756
Japanese yen	191.0
Luxembourg franc	47.71
New Zealand dollar	2.820
Norwegian crown	9.114
Portuguese escudo	204.7
Spanish peso	147.5
Swedish crown	8.437
Swiss franc	2.068
UK pound	0.816
US-Dollar	1.526

References

BRISSON, I. (1992), *Packaging Waste and the Environment: Economics and Policy*, CSERGE report 92-01, UCL London, UK.

EPA (1990), *Charging Households for Waste Collection and Disposals*, Washington DC, 1990.

HAHN, R.W. (1989), *Economic Prescriptions for Environmental problems: How the Patient followed the Doctor's Orders*, Journal of Economic Perspectives, Spring 1989, pp. 95-114.

HAHN, R.W. and HESTER, G.L. (1989), *Where Did All the Markets Go? An Analysis of EPA's Trading Program*, Yale Journal of Regulation, Winter 1989, pp. 109-153.

HOELLER, P. and COPPEL, J. (1992), *Energy Taxation and Price Distortions in Fossil Fuel Markets: Some Implications for Climate Change Policy*, OECD Economics Department, Working Paper no. 110, Paris.

KETE, N. (1991), "The US Acid Rain Control Allowance System", in, OECD, *Climate Change: Designing a Tradeable Permits System*, Paris.

MALAMAN, R. and RANCI, P. (1991), *Italian Environmental Policy*, paper presented at conference "Economy and Environment in the 90's", Neuchatel (Switz), August 26-27 1991.

MERRIFIELD, J.D. (1990), "A Critical Overview of the Evolutionary Approach to Air Pollution Abatement Policy", *Journal of Policy Analysis and Management*, 1990, pp. 367-380.

OATES, W.E., "Case Study on the United States", in OECD, *Environment and Taxation: The Cases of The Netherlands, Sweden, and the United States*, OECD, Paris (1994).

OECD (1993), "A comparison of carbon taxes in selected countries", OECD Environment monograph No. 78. Paris.

OPSCHOOR, J.B. and VOS, J.B. (1989), *Economic Instruments for Environmental Protection*, OECD Paris.

TIETENBERG, T.H. (1985), *Emissions Trading: an exercise in reforming pollution policy*, Resources for the Future, Washington D.C.

Chapter 4

Assessing Survey Outcomes

This chapter provides an overview and assessment of the foregoing chapter that has presented detailed survey outcomes of instruments functioning on 1-1-1992.

Section 4.1. gives an overview per policy instrument, and addresses the question of incentive effects. Section 4.2. provides an overview per country, showing that countries differ substantially in the degree of application of economic instruments. Section 4.3. attempts to review developments between the previous survey [Opschoor and Vos (1989)] and the present one. The final section (4.4) summarily describes a number of recent initiatives for new economic instruments.

4.1 Overview per policy instrument

4.1.1 *Charges on emissions (3.2)*

-- *User charges* (3.2.4 and 3.2.5.1) are quite common for waste collection and disposal and for sewerage and sewage treatment. User charges are a payment for services rendered.

-- *Municipal waste user charges* are levied in 18 countries, usually at flat rates for households and for firms on quantity of waste actually supplied. Data for firms are sketchy as presumably collection and disposal of industrial waste is normally privatized.

Increasingly evidence comes forward of municipalities experimenting with rates based on volume or weight of waste supplied [EPA (1990)].

-- *User charges for sewerage and sewage treatment* are levied in 17 countries, generally on the basis of water usage. The charges may have incentive effects if water usage is actually measured, as it usually is with industry. The incentive effect will be indirect though, as usage of water is charged rather than waste water emissions.

Data on water charges for households indicate a mixture of flat rates and metering. Seven countries base charges for firms not only on water usage but also on some measure of pollution load.

Table 4.1 **User charges**

	Municipal waste	Sewerage and sewage treatment
Australia	x	x
Austria	x	
Belgium	x	x
Canada	x	x
Denmark	x	x
Finland	x	x
France	x	x
Germany	x	x
Iceland	x	
Ireland		x
Italy	x	x
Japan	x	
Netherlands	x	x
New Zealand		x
Norway	x	x
Portugal		x
Spain	x	x
Sweden	x	x
Switzerland	x	x
UK		x
USA	x	x

Different from user charges, *emission charges* are levied regardless of actual effluent treatment.

In Table 4.2 the first symbol refers to intended incentive effects, the second to actual ones. For instance, with the Australian charge on hazardous waste incentive effects are intended, but no data are available on actual incentive effects.

Table 4.2 **Emission charges and taxes**

	Air	Aircraft noise	Soil	Waste	Hazardous waste	Water
Australia$_{reg}$				IU	I-	IU
Austria				F-	U-	
Belgium		F-	F-	I-	U-	IU
Canada$_{reg}$	(I)					I-
Denmark				II		
Finland					FF	
France	F-	(F)		U-		U-
Germany		IU				IU
Germany$_{reg}$				U-		
Italy				U-		
Japan	IU	F-				
Netherlands		F-	F-	(U)		FI
Norway	IU	I-				
Portugal	U-	F-			(FF)	F-
Spain						U-
Sweden	II					
Switzerland		F-				
USA	(I)					
USA$_{reg}$			I-		F-	

Key to symbols:
F   = Financing
I   = Incentive
U   = Unclear
-    = No data available
( ) = Proposal

As to the spending of charge revenue, earmarking (for environmental expenditure) is the general practice. 27 of the 33 charges listed in Table 4.2 have earmarked revenue, with 3 revenue spending is unknown and 3 charges are for the general budget. Table 4.3 summarizes the evidence on incentive effects of the charges listed in Table 4.2, distinguishing incentive effects intended and incentive effects actually demonstrated.

Table 4.3 **Incentive effects of emission charges and taxes**

	Incentive intended	Actual incentive effects
Yes	14	3
Inconclusive	8	7
No	12	1
No data	-	23

Table 4.3 shows primarily that little data is available on actual incentive effects. With 3 charges there is positive evidence of incentive effects. In seven cases the evidence is inconclusive, mainly because the charge is applied next to other policy instruments.

Table 4.4 **Tax differentiations on automobiles and gasoline**

	Car sales tax	Annual vehicle tax	Gasoline tax (lead content)
Austria		x	x
Belgium	x		x
Canada	x		x
Canada$_{reg}$	x		
Denmark		x	x
Finland	x		x
France			x
Germany	x	x	x
Greece	x		
Iceland			x
Ireland			x
Japan	x		
Netherlands	x	(x)	x
New Zealand			x
Norway	x		x
Portugal			x
Sweden	x		x
Switzerland			x
UK			x
USA	x		

4.1.2 *Charges on products (3.3)*

Tax differentiations are applied quite widely in motorcar transport. The car sales tax and annual vehicle tax differential applies to cars with and without catalytic converters.

In most countries market shares of unleaded petrol haven risen substantially after introduction of the tax differential. This may also have been due to other factors such as, the progressive market penetration of cars provided with catalytic converters and the falling market price of unleaded petrol. No data were available on the incentive impacts of the car sales tax and annual vehicle tax differential.

Table 4.5 gives the data on product charges that are not tax differentiations.

Table 4.5 **Product charges**

	Carbon	Sulphur in oil	Fertilizer	Pesticides	Batteries	Lubricant oil	CFC's	Packaging	Miscellaneous
Australia							FF		
Austria			FF				(F)		IU
Belgium							.	(I)	
Canada_{reg}								U-	I-,F-
Denmark	I-				FF		UU	IU	I-U-U-U-
Finland	U-		IU			FF			
France						FF			
Greece									FF
Italy	(U)					FF			II
Netherlan-ds	F-								FF
Norway	I-	IU	IU	I-		FF		II	
Sweden	IU	II	II	IU	FF			FF	IU,II,FF
USA							UI		FF
USA_{reg}									

Key to symbols:
I   = Incentive
F   = Financing
U   = Unclear
-    = No data available
( )   = Proposal

Table 4.6 summarizes the evidence on incentive effects of product charges.

Table 4.6 **Incentive effects of product charges**

	Incentive intended	Actual incentive effects
Yes	21	7
Inconclusive	8	10
No	22	20
No data	-	14

Concerning charges with intended incentive effects there is little evidence of actual incentive effects. This is due to a lack of research on the one hand, and the inconclusiveness of data on incentive impacts on the other hand. Data on incentive impacts are inconclusive in cases where the charge is applied in conjunction with other policy instruments, and no data are available on the separate effects of the charge.

4.1.3   Deposit refunds (3.4)

Table 4.7 **Deposit refund systems**

	Car hulks	Metal cans	Plastic bottles	Glass bottles	Miscellaneous
Australia$_{reg}$		x	x	x	
Austria			x	x	x
Belgium				x	
Canada				x	
Canada$_{reg}$		x	x		
Denmark			x	x	
Finland			x	x	x
Germany			x	x	(x)
Greece	x				
Iceland			x	x	
Netherlands			x	x	
Norway	x		x	x	
Portugal		x	x	x	
Sweden	x	x	x	x	
Switzerland				x	
Turkey				x	
USA$_{reg}$		x	x	x	x

Deposit refunds function mainly in the area of beverage packaging. Return percentages vary between 40 and 100 per cent, and are on average near 80 per cent.

4.1.4.   Tradeable permits (3.5)

Tradeable permit systems include permits formally tradeable, bubble policies and tradeable production rights (*e.g.*, CFC production quota in the USA).

Table 4.8 gives the number of tradeable permit systems per country.

Table 4.8 Tradeable permits

Country	Tradeable permit systems
Australia$_{reg}$	x
Canada	x,x
Germany	x
USA	x,x,x,x,x
USA$_{reg}$	x,x,x

The US Emissions Trading program has achieved cost savings, but the number of trades has remained limited and most trades have been intra-company. The limited effects are due to the restricted scope of the program (allowing only trading of emission reductions beyond regulatory baselines), the trading rules (promoting primarily intra-company trading) and the uncertainty created by the joint application of discretionary command and control regulation next to the tradeable permit program. The Acid Rain Control Allowance program, functioning from 1993 on, has more the characteristics of a full blown tradeable permit program. The results of this program will therefore be of great interest.

4.1.5 Enforcement incentives (3.6)

Enforcement incentives include performance bonds and penalty fees of which rates are not fixed, but depend on damage inflicted or non-compliance benefits reaped.

Table 4.9 gives the number of enforcement incentives per country.

Table 4.9 Enforcement incentives

Country	Performance bonds	Penalty fees
Australia$_{reg}$	x,x	
Canada		x
Canada$_{reg}$	x	
Sweden		x,x
USA		x,x,(x)

Note :   Data on incentive effects are not available.

4.2 Overview per country

Table 4.10 provides a summary of the application of economic instruments per country.

For Australia, Belgium, Canada and the USA instruments applied at non-federal level have been included.

The table should be interpreted with the greatest care, as "policy instruments" within one instrument type are simply added up while in fact their relative importance differs a great deal. For instance, the US Emissions Trading Program, covering tens of thousands of sources, involving hundreds of trades and consisting of various sub programs (bubbles, netting, offsets, banking), counts as "one" tradeable permit system just as the "Plant Renewal Clause" in German air pollution which is essentially a netting provision that has hardly been implemented so far.

For charges, revenue and GDP data could figure as weights, but revenue data were not consistently available.

Between instrument types (charges, deposit refunds) the differences are even more obvious. There is not much point in aggregating, for instance, the Dutch water effluent charge and the deposit refund on PET-bottles. This is why the columns have not been added.

With federalized countries (Australia, Belgium, Canada, Germany and the USA) instruments applied at non-federal level, *i.e.*, in one or more provinces or states, have been included. For instance, in the USA and Australia nine instruments are "non-federal", in Canada seven and also a number in Australia. This is one of the reasons why these countries figure highly in Table 4.10.

When account is taken of the number of non-federal instruments included in the data for Australia, Canada and the USA, Table 4.10 shows that the Scandinavian countries are leading in the application of economic instruments, especially charges. The USA is ahead in the application of the tradeable permits instrument.

While countries at the top of the Table generally do have ambitious environmental policies, it is not true, judging from the data for Germany, Switzerland and Japan, that conversely, all countries with ambitious environmental policies apply economic instruments extensively.

Data on charge revenues were not consistently available. Below some data are presented, derived from responses to questionnaires and OECD-tax revenue statistics of member countries.

Table 4.10 Economic instruments per country on 1-1-1992

	Charges on emissions (of which user charges)	Charges on products (of which tax differentiations)	Deposit refunds	Tradeable permits	Enforcement incentives
USA	5 (2)	6 (1)	4	8	2
Sweden	3 (2)	11 (2)	4		2
Canada	3 (2)	7 (3)	1	2	2
Denmark	3 (2)	10 (2)	2		
Finland	3 (2)	10 (2)	2		
Norway	4 (2)	8 (2)	3		
Australia	5 (2)	1 (0)	3	1	2
Netherlands	5 (2)	4 (2)	2		
Austria	3 (1)	4 (2)	3		
Germany	5 (2)	3 (3)	2	1	
Belgium	7 (2)	2 (2)	1		
France	5 (2)	2 (1)			
Switzerland	3 (2)	2 (2)	1		
Italy	3 (2)	2 (0)			
Iceland	1 (1)	1 (1)	2		
Japan	3 (1)	1 (1)			
Portugal	2 (0)	1 (1)	1		
Ireland	2 (2)	1 (1)			
Greece		2 (1)	1		
Spain	3 (2)				
UK	1 (1)	1 (1)			
New Zealand	1 (1)				
Turkey			1		

For all countries except Finland and the Netherlands charge revenue are exclusive of user charges.

In Sweden, revenue of environmental charges was around 0.75 per cent of GDP in 1991. The CO_2 charge accounted for 0.65 per cent alone. In fact, the Swedish CO_2 charge is part of an integral system of energy taxation with substantial revenue. General energy taxes are however, not included in this survey.

In Denmark environmental charges, excluding the carbon tax, account for around 0.15 per cent of GDP.

Norwegian revenue of environmental charges is 0.75 per cent of GDP.

In the Netherlands the revenue from environmental charges, including the water pollution charge, is 0.6 per cent of GDP. The water pollution charge alone accounts for 0.4 per cent.

In Finland revenue of environmental charges including user charges was 0.9 per cent of GDP in 1992. Excluding user charges revenue is 0.4 per cent of GDP.

In the USA, revenue of the CFC charge and the hazardous waste charge (Superfund) amounted to 0.3 per cent of GDP in 1991.

4.3 Developments between 1987 and 1992

Comparing the survey results with the previous survey of economic instruments [(Opschoor and Vos (1989)], that took stock of the state of affairs in 1987, is difficult for the following reasons:

-- More countries are covered in the present survey.
   In this survey data from 23 countries are included, compared to 15 in the 1987-survey;
-- Apart from responses to the questionnaire, many more data sources have been used now (*cf*. Appendix I, Chapter 3);
-- The coverage of instruments in the present survey is more restricted.
   The present survey does not deal with subsidies, administrative charges and environmental liability;
-- As data on rates and tariffs are far from complete, progressive rises of charge rates, conceivably implying increased incentive impact, are not documented satisfactorily.

Nevertheless, a rough comparison is possible for 8 countries that have been surveyed in detail in the previous and the present survey.

Changes have been minor in France, Germany and Italy, moderate in the Netherlands and Norway and extensive in Finland, Sweden and the USA.

France has instituted a tax differential on leaded and unleaded car petrol. A tax on waste has been introduced, while the noise charge has been temporarily rescinded awaiting a revision of the charge formula. In Germany a differentiation of car vehicle taxes has been introduced and there are now waste disposal taxes in some Federal states. In Italy no new economic instruments have been implemented. In 1989/1990 a set of proposals for economic instruments was rejected by Parliament.

From Table 4.11 the picture for the Netherlands is deceptive, as since the previous survey a number of minor charges have been lumped together in the already existing General Fuel charge, which has been raised substantially while the earmarking of revenue has been rescinded. In 1990 a task force was instituted to engage in feasibility research for a number of economic instruments. As yet no new instruments have been introduced, but policy debates are going on, especially on an energy-carbon tax. Presently two proposals are pending for charges on groundwater and waste. Economic incentives (charges and tradeable permits) for reducing mineral emissions in agriculture are being considered.

Norway has rescinded a charge on batteries and instituted a carbon tax and a charge on aircraft noise. A deposit refund on plastic beverage bottles has been introduced. Together with the Netherlands Norway is active in promoting international interest in economic incentives for abating greenhouse gas emissions.

Finland and Sweden have actually implemented a range of new product charges, to a considerable extent with incentive purposes.

Finland instituted charges on carbon, batteries, fertilizer and diesel oil and implemented a deposit refund on plastic bottles. In the government service there is a permanent committee for investigating and proposing environmental charges.

Table 4.11. Comparing 1987 and 1992

	Charges on emissions		Charges on products		Deposit refunds		Tradeable permits		Enforcement incentives	
	1987	1992	1987	1992	1987	1992	1987	1992	1987	1992
Finland	3	3	6	10	1	3	-	-	-	-
France	5	5	1	2	-	-	-	-	-	-
Germany	5	4	2	3	1	2	1	1	-	-
Italy	3	3	2	2	-	-	-	-	-	-
Netherlands	6	5	5	4	2	2	-	-	-	-
Norway	2	4	8	8	2	3	-	-	-	-
Sweden	3	3	7	11	3	4	-	-	2	2
USA	4	5	?	6	?	4	3	8	1	2

Before 1991 Sweden introduced a differentiation of car sales taxes, a fuel charge on domestic aviation and a deposit refund on PET-bottles. In 1991 the Swedish tax system was reformed, involving tax revenues of around 6 per cent of GDP. The reform consisted amongst others of a broadening of the VAT-base (to energy products) and environmental charges on energy products, decreasing personal income taxation and the existing general tax on energy products correspondingly. The new environmental charges include a carbon tax, a tax on sulphur in fuels, a tax differentiation of petroleum products and a charge on NO_x emissions of energy producers.

A major role in the development of new economic instruments was played by the Environmental Charge Commission, instituted in 1988 and consisting of parliamentarians, government officials and independent experts. The Commission has published various reports and has been very active in proposing new instruments.

Since 1987 the USA have, at the Federal level, deployed the instrument of tradeable emission rights to the control of ozone depleting chemicals and SO_2 emissions and in three programs of more limited scope. A charge on ozone depleting chemicals has been instituted, next to the tradeable consumption and production quota system, in order to skim off windfall profits resulting from the forced production cutback. With the revision of the Clean Air Act new opportunities for economic instruments have been created, *e.g.*, from 1993 on, States are authorized to levy permit fees on the basis of recorded emissions. In the present survey a number of product charges and deposit refunds are included that are applied by US States.

4.4 Recent national and international initiatives

In OECD-countries official interest in economic instruments is rising. This can be inferred from the data presented so far, as well as from recent initiatives.

In 1992 the OECD published guidelines for the application of economic instruments [OECD (1992)].

In eight countries official task forces are carrying out feasibility studies. In addition six countries have stated a general intention to apply economic instruments increasingly [de Savornin Lohman (1991)].

In international fora taxes and tradeable permits for greenhouse gas abatement are on the agenda.

The European Commission has accepted a proposal for an energy-carbon tax, to be implemented conditional on implementation of fiscal incentives by major trading partners.

In the USA President Clinton's administration has proposed an energy tax.

In Belgium a set of product charges is to be implemented on 1-1-1994, on disposable beverage packaging, pesticides, paper and disposable razors and photo cameras. Switzerland is considering incentive charges on volatile organic compounds, sulphur content of heating oil, fertilizers, pesticides and batteries.

Austria is considering a charge on waste water, fiscal incentives to reduce chlorine emissions, a deposit refund for refrigerators and an energy/carbon tax.

Denmark, Finland and Sweden are continually adapting their systems of fiscal incentives. In Germany there is a permanent policy debate on economic incentives in waste management and transport.

The UK is considering charges on waste water and in the area of waste management.

4.5 Discussion of 1987 prospects

Along with the 1987 survey, some expectations with respect to future developments in the use of economic instruments have been formulated. This section attempts to evaluate these prospects against the main results of the present survey. Expectations emerging from the 1987-survey are summarised, firstly in general, and secondly on an instrument-by-instrument basis and compared with the present situation. We will conclude this section with a short discussion of developments in selected countries.

4.5.1 Economic instruments in general

The 1987 survey noticed that a number of policy tendencies were visible, which could have an impact on the role of economic instruments. These were:

a) A tendency towards reduced government intervention (deregulation) could lead to a more prominent role of economic instruments, in particular charges. Charges may provide incentives to change polluters behaviour in a more generic way, and may raise revenues for (self)-financing of environmental measures;

b) A tendency towards policy integration could induce harmonisation of economic instruments applied in different policy sectors, and development of new, broad-based economic instruments;

c) A shift of attention from curative to preventive policies could result in a stronger role for instruments such as product charges, and deposit-refund systems.

Indeed, the role of charges has been extended, although their revenue raising capabilities have remained the dominant function. Although an increasing number of charge schemes show incentive purposes, not much evidence exists that such instruments will replace direct regulation, as part of a process towards reducing government intervention. Extension of the number of deposit-refund systems might be a signal of intensifying attempts of governments to shift responsibility for packaging waste to the societal parties concerned, and to reduce their own role.

Policy integration has shown progress, but this is hardly reflected in the role of economic instruments. The rise of carbon taxes may be considered as an example, since it is an instrument of both environmental policy and of energy policy. The 1987 survey pointed to the desirability of harmonisation of instruments that affect prices in the EC Member States, with a view to the completion of the internal market, resulting in opening up of the national borders. The E.C Commission has devoted considerable attention to the issue of economic instruments, culminating in a proposal for a CO_2/energy tax, to be introduced if trade partners would take comparable measures. No other proposals are currently being considered in EC bodies.

Although curative policy is still a major policy issue, preventive policies have gained in importance. Presently, more product charges and deposit-refund systems are in operation than in 1987, which may underline this tendency.

The 1987 survey also discussed the desirability that economic instruments be extended towards the field of multi-pollutant and intermedia pollution problems, such as acidification, but it was added that there was not much evidence for such a development. One of the few examples where this development has materialised regards the Acid Rain Allowance Trading scheme in the USA.

4.5.2   Charges

In 1987 the financial function of charges predominated. This was concluded mainly on the basis of the generally low levels of the charge rates, and evidence suggested that this would not change drastically. As was concluded above, this has appeared to be correct in general, although the number of incentive charges with substantial charge rates has increased. Some examples concern the CO_2 charges in Denmark, Norway and Sweden, the Swedish NO_x charge, the Danish waste disposal charge, and a number of product charges (on fertilizers in Sweden, on ozone depleting chemicals in the USA, on packaging in Finland and Norway). Tax differentials on sales' prices of new cars with catalysts and on unleaded petrol may well have contributed to the rapid penetration of these products on the market.

4.5.3   Deposit-refund systems

Deposit-refund systems were considered to be promising instruments, for example within the framework of preventive policies and of policy deregulation. Indeed, the number of schemes increased substantially since the 1987 survey, in which some doubts were expressed about chances for new systems. The reason was that some traditional systems appeared to be phased-out in favour of one-way packaging, as a consequence of private cost-benefit analyses. A remarkable development is with regards to the introduction of deposit-refund systems for plastic bottles. These were hardly mentioned in the 1987 survey. The present inventory shows a widespread application in at least 11 countries.

4.5.4   Emissions trading

The 1987 survey expressed the expectation that in the USA emissions trading policies would take a more liberal course in the near future. Indeed, new systems have been implemented for CFC's and Acid Rain control.

As a consequence of crucial differences between the structure of environmental policy in the USA and in Europe, not much development in introducing trading schemes was expected in Europe. In fact, only Germany currently applies a trading scheme which was already in operation in 1987. It has also been stated, then, that increasing problems with, for example, acidification, might nevertheless create new opportunities. This has not been the case for acidification, but presently trading schemes on a global level are envisaged for greenhouse gases. Emissions trading in the field of water quality policy were called promising. However, no new applications have emerged since 1987.

110

References

OPSCHOOR, J.B and H.B. VOS (1989), *Economic Instruments for Environmental Protection*, OECD, Paris.

DE SAVORNIN LOHMAN A.(1991), "Financial investment and economic incentives in OECD countries", Paper presented to The Business Council for Sustainable Development workshop, *Economic Investment from the Business Perspective*, London, July 12-14 1991.

EPA (1990), *Charging Households for Waste Collection and Disposals*, Washington D.C.

OCDE (1991), *Environmental Policy: How to Apply Economic Instruments,* OECD, Paris.

Chapter 5

Analysis of Operational Economic Instruments

5.1 Introduction

In previous chapters extensive attention has been given to the use of economic instruments in OECD Member States. Chapters 6 through 8 are devoted to possibilities of effective applications of economic instruments in economies in transition and in the field of global environmental problems, and to international trade aspects of economic instruments. In the present chapter the focus will be on operational aspects of economic instruments in environmental policy. The purpose of this chapter is to analyze criteria and circumstances which might be useful when considering the choice and introduction of economic instruments in a practical policy framework. It attempts a down-to-earth analysis which may provide some guidance for decision-making, recognizing the institutional and practical factors to be taken into account in a real-world decision environment.

The approach followed in this chapter has two dimensions. First, indicating directions for the choice and structure of economic instruments which should be based on, *inter alia*, economic principles. Second, experiences with economic instruments in operation may reveal a number of practical aspects which can be used when designing new applications of economic instruments to certain environmental problems. New applications of economic instruments may be preceded by thorough *ex-ante* evaluation, in which results from *ex-post* evaluation of comparable cases might provide useful inputs.

The analysis in this chapter comprises investigation of criteria for the choice of instruments for specific policy contexts and discusses an approach for distinguishing specific application context characteristics as checkpoints for guidance of instruments choice (Section 5.2). Section 5.3 attempts to list some practical aspects to be taken on board, as they appeared from application of economic instruments described in chapter 3. This chapter concludes with an attempt to apply the approach developed to the case of packaging waste management (Section 5.4).

The analysis of this chapter is by no means intended to provide a set of guidelines which would be generally applicable in each and every context of application. It is meant to illustrate a possible way of dealing with the choice of instruments in a practical context.

5.2 The choice of instruments

5.2.1 Basic criteria

As has been pointed out in chapters 1 and 2, economists have claimed a number of advantages of market-based instruments over "command-and control" type instruments. They have done, and continue to do so with reference to the neo-classical theorem that an optimal allocation of resources will ensue from correct and comprehensive pricing in the marketplace, including the pricing of environmental commodities. In other words, in this approach **efficiency** is the basic criterion to be applied. Since environmental goods are normally not priced "by nature", taxes could be imposed on the use of such goods in order to correct this failure. If correctly assessed, such taxes would be inherently efficient, and thus effective for that matter. Tradeable permits can be equally efficient in principle, although these instruments do not depart from prices but allot pollution rights, based on allowable levels of pollution, leading to correct pricing.

As a result of fundamental and empirical problems, pricing of environmental goods through taxation can only be a second-best solution. Hence, the efficiency of economic instruments is not automatically secured. A separate and major criterion for judgement of policy instruments in the environmental field is effectiveness, which is tested by comparing the results of instruments with objectives set by authorities, *i.e.*, environmental goals.

Environmental effectiveness and *economic efficiency* are major evaluation criteria. Obviously, efficiency also includes costs of administration, related to implementation and enforcement. The fact that such costs are mostly overlooked, or at least not exhaustively inventoried in many instrument analyses, however, justifies explicit attention.

Social and legal objectives of government policy require that policy instruments also satisfy the criterion of *acceptability* which encompasses distributional impacts (equity), transparency and concordance with institutional frameworks. The issue of distributional impacts is relevant, as it is a major determinant of acceptability of instruments by target groups who will have to cooperate in implementation. Economic instruments may also affect income distribution which is an economic policy subject in many countries. Transparency ensures that target groups have a clear view of the rationale for introduction of the instrument and of the environmental purpose to be served. The institutional framework requires that instruments are concordant with important policy principles, like the Polluter Pays Principle, and to major institutional constructions, like the fiscal framework. Supra-national treaties may imply restrictions with respect to the application of economic instruments by treaty parties, such as prohibition of trade and competition distorting charges and prohibition of charges which require border control. Acceptability is also a major prerequisite for effective enforcement.

Criteria such as efficiency, effectiveness and acceptability as described above have a general significance, but they mostly lack in operationality in cases of practical choice and design of instruments. Quantitative testing of efficiency and effectiveness requires a model in which application of alternative policy instruments in a given policy context is compared with a base-line or reference situation. Such models are normally not sufficiently detailed for application in a micro-economic framework. Instead of exhaustive model specification, one may elaborate on basic criteria in order to attempt to come up with a set of more operational criteria or characteristics for a practical instrument choice and design.

Before turning to a more pragmatic decision analysis framework, we briefly summarize some practical points mentioned in the literature with regard to application of specific economic instruments.

5.2.2   *Practical aspects of economic instruments*

Many authors have dealt with practical aspects of choice and design of environmental policy instruments [among many others Stavins, (1990), Tietenberg, (1992), Government of Canada, (1992)]. A general approach to examine such aspects can be found in OECD (1991). The latter focused on

114

economic instruments and took an overall approach, covering, among other items, circumstances in which specific economic instruments could be of use.

In summary, it concluded that **emissions charges** could be particularly appropriate in cases of a restricted number of stationary sources where monitoring of emissions is feasible. Emission charges can be an efficient instrument, when marginal abatement costs vary across polluters, provided that polluters are able to react to financial incentives. A major condition is the potential for technological innovation.

Product charges are potentially applicable to products that pollute in the consumption phase. Such products should be identifiable, and consumed in large quantities and in diffuse patterns. Product charges can also be used as a proxy for emission charges in those cases in which the conditions listed above are not fulfilled. A specific form of product charges, *i.e.*, tax differentiation, could be successfully applied in cases where polluting products should be progressively replaced by a simply identifiable and readily available, less polluting substitute.

Deposit-refund systems can be considered for products or substances which can be reused, recycled or which must be returned for destruction after use.

Tradeable emission rights offer advantages in situations in which marginal abatement costs differ among polluters, and in which maximum ceilings to total pollution are urgently required. Then, the application of generic standards can seriously obstruct economic development. If the number of parties involved is large enough to establish well-functioning markets, a relative or even absolute least-cost pollution reduction can be achieved in growing commodity markets.

A decision analysis framework

An attempt to systematically analyze at an operational level the choice of instruments should start with establishing a general analysis framework in which the basic criteria listed above play a fundamental role as background for operational guidance. Such a general framework might consist of three stages:

a) An analysis of conditions external to the context of application, such as requirements from related government policy fields, and of possible, strong, mainly pollution-related, characteristics which might be overriding with respect to the choice of instruments.

b) A general analysis of the context of application itself for which an adequate instrument must be chosen, and a selection of types of instruments which could be considered feasible.

c) A detailed and operational analysis in which all practical aspects relevant to the context of application and to goals and impacts of the instruments analyzed are taken into account, resulting in a proposal for the design of a specific instrument (or combination of instruments, or adjuncts to existing instruments) to be used.

Each of the stages mentioned is dealt with hereafter. The emphasis will be on stage 2 which, in our view, is a major steps to be taken towards operationality of economic instruments.

Stage 1: external elements and overriding conditions

Firstly, stage 1 deals with external analysis elements. External elements reflect relevant factors outside the policy problem for which the analysis is made. Environmental policy does not operate in isolation from other government policies. External elements could comprise a broad range of factors, including economic, fiscal and international policies. In the framework of policy integration other policy fields can also be relevant, *e.g.*, those of energy, transport and agriculture. Extensive treatment of these external elements is beyond the scope of this chapter.

Secondly, overriding conditions may restrict policy options. Such conditions may include (see also Opschoor and Pearce, (1991)]:

a) harmful environmental (*e.g.*, toxic) impacts;
b) short-term problems;
c) great risks and uncertainties.

These aspects are pollution-related. In these circumstances the use of direct regulation (bans, strict standards) is advocated, because we are in a situation, where effectiveness of the instrument is by far the most important decision criterion. Enforcement is of decisive importance.

Stage 2: analysis of context of application

With regard to the context of application to be examined, two sets of concrete internal elements are basic to environmental policy situations in which one must decide on instruments. They relate to i) sources of pollution, and to ii) polluting substances and their environmental impact. These internal elements, or context-specific characteristics, should have a relationship with the decision criteria mentioned earlier. They might be considered as indicators for potentially effective, efficient and acceptable application of policy instruments. The following list of characteristics [based on Bovenberg *et al*, (1991), and WRR, (1992)] is by no means exhaustive, but serves as an example.

Characteristics related to sources of pollution:

- Number and variety of sources
- Costs of compliance and variety therein
- Scale of the market and (international) competitiveness
- Availability of alternative processes and products
- Potential for technological innovation

Characteristics related to polluting substances and environmental impacts:

- Recognizability of pollution/opportunity for monitoring
- Structure of the linkage between emissions and environmental impact (carrying capacity/thresholds)

Measures of these characteristics could indicate how instruments would score in terms of evaluation criteria. For example, in a situation with a large number of sources which vary in size and in relative costs of compliance, economic instruments might be more efficient than direct regulation. However, if these sources operate on an international market, substantial charges unilaterally implemented would not be acceptable. If sources compete with foreign firms in the domestic market, then emission charges would negatively influence competitiveness, whereas product charges would not. Generic, rigid charges may not be effective, if alternative, less-polluting processes or products are not available. Gradual strengthening of standards may be advisable. If a strong case for technological innovation exists, charges might create a dynamic impulse for innovation.

If recognizability of pollution is low, *e.g.*, with respect to diffuse sources, charges or tradeable permits may create large administration costs, negatively affecting efficiency. In cases where no linear relationship exists between emissions and environmental impact, *e.g.*, when a threshold exists below which emissions do not create environmental damage, charges and tradeable permits could be a non efficient solution. An exhaustive list of possible interrelations between situation-specific characteristics and decision criteria is beyond the scope of this chapter.

Application contexts can also be discerned which differ with respect to the relative weights given to evaluation criteria. Lave and Gruenspecht (1991) have described a number of such application contexts. If, for example, a "no risk" decision framework is chosen, the emphasis is on environmental effectiveness. Another example relates to the case of a "cost-effectiveness" framework. Then, also explicit attention is given to the efficiency criterion.

To further illustrate the relevance of different contexts of application, we refer to an example of an implementation oriented, indicative approach, developed by the Dutch Scientific Council for Government Policy in a recent report on environmental policy instruments [WRR, (1992)]. It attempts to translate specific characteristics of application contexts to indications of what types of instruments to apply.

The approach developed by WRR departs from the assumption that instruments should be tuned to general characteristics, which are inherent in any context of application, and which can be subdivided into three groups (see also the characteristics mentioned above):

a) Characteristics related to the recognizability of emissions (possibility of monitoring) and of environmental impacts;

b) Characteristics related to the structure of the target group. Market structure and competitiveness are relevant issues in this respect;

c) Characteristics determining the resistance in the target group against the instrument investigated. Among these, costs and characteristics of demand (*e.g.*, elasticities) play a major role.

WRR distinguishes and characterizes a number of distinct contexts of application by varying the values of the main characteristics as discerned above. As indicators for the groups of characteristics, they use: i) monitoring of emissions, ii) number of sources, and iii) relative costs and cost differences of compliance. These indicators are all source-related. Table 5.1 presents an overview of these application contexts, which have been given names for characterizing.

Table 5.1. **Seven distinct application contexts and the possible choice of instruments**

Context of application	Monitoring of emissions	Number of sources	Costs of compliance	Suggested policy instruments
"Clear"	Good	Low	Low	DR
"Distribution"	Good	Low	High	EI
"Manageable"	Good	High	Low	EI/SI
"Heterogeneous"	Good	High	High	Ei
"Invisible"	Poor	Low	High	DR
"Diffuse"	Poor	High	Low	SI
"Complex	Poor	High	High	?

Notes :   DR = Direct regulation; EI = Economic instruments; SI = Suasive instruments

Source: adapted from WRR (1992)

To conclude the description of stage 2, illustrations of some of these application contexts are given and suggestions for possible policy instruments are made. These examples are derived from WRR (1992). Section 5.4 presents a similar though more elaborated analysis of the packaging waste management issue.

Emissions of acidifying substances by power generation plants can be characterized as a "distribution" problem application context, in which a small number of sources emit pollutants which can be relatively easily monitored. Costs of abatement are high, and may vary considerably among (old and new) sources. Here, economic instruments, notably emission charges, could be an appropriate instrument. Common standards are less efficient and implementation of emission charges does not create large administrative burdens.

A reverse situation occurs with regard to the problem of **litter in natural areas** ("diffuse" application context). A large number of sources, difficult to monitor, for which costs of compliance are low. Here, suasive instruments could be advisable, because other types of instruments would not work properly, due to monitoring problems and inaccessibility of sources. Moreover, if costs of compliance are low, "soft" instruments do have a chance.

The case of ***reducing CFC emissions*** could be described as a "manageable" context of application, in which a high number of sources would probably face relatively low costs of compliance. However, if it is assumed that production of CFCs could act as a proxy for emissions, monitoring of pollution at a low number of sources (producers) would be relatively easy. Then, both a product charge and suasive instruments, or a combination, could be envisaged. Other factors like urgency of compliance, however, may render non-coercive instruments unreliable.

CO_2 emissions by residential heating are a similar case, but for the fact that costs of compliance with reduction targets are relatively high. This case is indicated as a "heterogeneous" context of application. A product charge on energy could be envisaged, possibly in combination with suasive instruments. The latter would probably be ineffective, if applied alone.

Comment: "mixed" applications

In practice, the choice of instruments will of course also be influenced by instruments that are already applied. Combinations of various types of instruments ("mixed" applications) can be advantageous for a number of reasons [OECD, (1989), (1991)]. Firstly, adding an economic instrument can provide an additional dynamic incentive for compliance over and above compulsory, but often static direct regulations. Secondly, economic instruments may precede adjustments of existing or new direct regulations. The definition and implementation of direct regulation takes time, in particular where it concerns legislation on the international/national level. Thirdly, combinations of different types of economic instruments might create a forceful instrument, *e.g.*, a combination of a deposit-refund system and a product charge on non-returnable products. Finally, keeping direct regulation or economic instruments as alternative options may play a stimulative role in negotiations aimed at achieving voluntary agreements with industry for changing environmental behaviour.

Approaches in which contexts of applications are being characterized as to their suitability for applying certain types of environmental policy instruments should explicitly take into account advantages of "mixed" applications.

Stage 3: detailed operational analysis

The final stage of the decision analysis is a detailed operational analysis for fine-tuning the structure and operation of the instrument or combination of instruments selected earlier. An in-depth examination of this part of the analysis is beyond the scope of this chapter. Only a number of relevant issues are mentioned here.

a) Design of the structure of selected instruments concerning the type of charge (emission charge, product charge) and parameters like the charge base (encompassing defined products or pollutants) and charge rate (tariffs), level of deposits and refunds, relevant parameters of emissions trading systems.

b) Determination of relevant target groups under charge or emission trading systems, or the relevant actors in deposit-refund systems.

c) Design of policy and legislative procedures and information of and consultation with the parties concerned

d) Structuring an administrative organisation for implementation and enforcement.

e) Determination of implementation issues like announcement, definition of transition periods and information.

f) Assessment of (distribution of) costs, of revenues (in case of charges) and preparation of evaluation of environmental impacts.

5.3 Some practical experiences

The approach discussed in section 5.2 has mainly been the result of academic analysis. Practice may reveal experiences with economic instruments that might be of use in deciding on new applications. They are derived from chapter 3 in which economic instruments currently applied in OECD Member States have been described. First, some general observations are made.

a) With one or two exceptions, no integral results were found with respect to environmental effectiveness and economic efficiency of the instruments described. Major impediments for such an analysis are, the difficulties in measuring the results from instruments applied, as compared to alternative policies, and the lack of a quantitative inventory of the base-line environmental situation.

b) Experiences listed below sometimes seem obvious, but nevertheless may provide useful elements for various practical cases.

c) Experiences described are restricted to those which are relatively new, or at least differ from the evaluation presented in the previous OECD-report on guidelines for economic instruments [OECD, (1991)].

5.3.1   Charges

a) A first observation with regard to the application of charges is that, with respect to charges having a stated incentive purpose, revenue raising capacities still prevail in many instances. Incentive objectives of such charges appear to be of secondary importance. This implies that very few cases exist from which practical experiences with regard to effectiveness and efficiency can be derived. Evaluations of real incentive charges are highly recommendable.

b) The Swedish charge on NOx provides an example of an emission charge with incentive impact and is based on actual monitoring of emissions. Revenues of the charge are directly rebated. In its first year (1992), effectiveness of the charge has surpassed expectations, resulting in a shortfall of funds for rebate. This charge system could be considered as a test case. An evaluation is due in 1994.

c) The Danish waste disposal charge is another example of an incentive charge based on actual monitoring. In its first version, some waste materials were exempted from the charge. As a result of practical problems with correctly determining these materials, exemptions were withdrawn in the second version, so that all waste disposed of is eligible to the charge. For materials that are carried off, a rebate is received. Sometimes debates arise about the definition of waste and about the correctness of rebates in certain cases. It appears that such charges should have a well-defined field of operation, including a charge base as simple as possible, with clear exemptions to the barest minimum. Also cases for rebates must be clear.

d) The necessity of simple implementation schemes is obvious from a number of applications. The Danish waste charge is one example. The Norwegian charge on batteries, abolished in 1992, had an equal charge rate for each type of battery, from pen-light to car batteries. Although intended for regulating the use of batteries, administrative processes demanded a simple scheme. Customs authorities who were charged with implementation of the charge system, were not prepared to distinguish between many types of batteries when establishing charges for each separate shipment. It is sometimes difficult to balance effectiveness and simplicity, or (administrative) efficiency.

e) Purely incentive charges in particular will be considered as (para)fiscal charges, and the revenues as fiscal revenues, to be added to the public budget. Such charges must fit in with the fiscal system, and must satisfy certain, sometimes strict, rules. Moreover, if goals are not clearly set, charges may not survive due to a lack of acceptability, *e.g.*, lack of concordance with institutional frameworks. This was apparent in a number of practical cases. In the Swedish NO_x charge system, reimbursement is an important element for acceptability. The high rates of the Dutch water pollution charge are acceptable, because of the transparent spending of the revenues. Adding the revenues of the Danish product charge on milk cartons to the public budget was questioned, when it appeared that the charge had no incentive impact.

f) Tax differentiation with regard to cars and gasoline, applied in many European countries, has worked well, since costs for parties involved were relatively low. New technology was already available at the moment of introduction of the incentives, at least in Europe, since Japanese and USA regulations were well ahead. Leaded RON 92 gasoline could easily be replaced by unleaded RON 95 gasoline.

g) The Danish system of product charges has shown that a product charge on glass bottles, aimed at increasing the number of trips of bottles in the deposit-refund system, has encouraged wine bottlers to pack their products in cartons which face a much lower charge. A high charge on new returnable bottles favours the use of returned bottles, but also the use of one-way containers. Substitutes for the charged product must be carefully examined with respect to their environmental impacts.

5.3.2   *Deposit-refund systems*

a) Still very few applications of deposit-refund systems are found outside the field of packaging for beverages. It is not clear why, but maintaining traditional systems and turning them into systems for environmental purposes may have played an important role here. This indicates that deposit-refund systems could be used more frequently, should advantages be clear in specific cases.

b) Next to old deposit-refund systems for beverage containers (*e.g.*, for glass bottles), new systems (*e.g.*, for PET bottles) appear to show high percentages of return, at least for relatively cheap drinks such as beer and soft drinks. Returns are still substantially worse for wine and liquors where the deposit is a small portion of the sales price of the beverage. Finland is an exception.

c) Both the Swedish, privately managed, DRS on drink cans and the Danish system for beer, soft drinks and wine show that handling costs for retailers can be substantial. Fair handling fees can enhance the acceptability of such systems for handlers.

5.3.3 Tradeable permits[1]

a) Except for a few cases in Australia, the use of tradeable permits in environmental policy is still limited to the USA, where a number of specific applications provide some flexibility for individual firms with regard to "command-and-control" regulation in US air quality policy. Experiences are derived from the applications described in chapter 3 (Emissions Trading, Acid rain Allowance Trading, Production and Consumption Rights of Ozone Depleting Substances, Water Pollution Trading) and from the Lead-in-Gasoline Trading scheme which was successfully completed in 1987.

b) The Lead Trading case is considered to be a successful and effective application, due in part to the fact that requirements with regard to lead contents in gasoline, as well as a time-path for reduction, were previously set. Hence, it was clear when factual reductions were eligible for credits. Contrary evidence exists with regard to the Emissions Trading scheme, where emissions ceilings are not always exactly defined, leaving room for differing interpretations of emission reduction credits.

c) A central characteristic of emissions trading is its contribution to efficiency of individual measures to be adopted under environmental policy. Basic to trading is a well-functioning market. Existing schemes have shown a number of problems here. Within the Emissions Trading scheme it has appeared that obscurity about concrete emission reduction credits and the way they can be traded and banked will prevent a lively market, since market parties are not prepared to run the risks. Again, the Lead Trading case has shown a well-functioning market, especially in the final stage of the phase-down.

d) A major condition for a fully efficient trading program is a large and well-functioning market. Nevertheless, trading programs may offer some measure of benefit even when they are limited in scope or encumbered by complex regulatory procedures, as long as there are at least two emitters eligible to trade and they have a large disparity between their compliance costs.

e) Restriction of individual market power may sometimes be necessary for a well-functioning market. Special provisions for accommodating new entrants may also be needed if initial rights are grandfathered to existing companies. In the Ozone Depleting Substances case, where two producers dominate the market, concentration of market power was prevented by allotting initial rights to all market parties, and by restricting the growth of individual packages to 10 per cent of their initial values. Moreover, a provision was made for new market parties (a "market of last resort"). These elements are also applied in the Acid Rain Trading scheme.

f) Monitoring, record-keeping and reporting are critical elements of a trading program. Adequate enforcement may require significant upgrading of these activities, which is sometimes costly or technically difficult. A register of participants and of transactions is necessary to keep track of the system. A reliable data base on initial emissions is needed in order to get the system started. The Lead Trading scheme showed that sometimes problems occur with respect to small sources. In the Acid Rain programme only large sources will participate. They are obliged to install a "Continuous Emissions Monitoring System".

---

1. Some of the experiences described in this section have been derived from Vos *et al.* (1992).

g) Acceptability of trading schemes may be promoted through grandfathering which is generally applied in trading programs that have been implemented to date and in schemes that are currently developed.

5.4 Economic instruments for packaging waste management: a pilot study(2)

5.4.1 Introduction

The final section of this chapter is devoted to an attempt to apply elements of the analysis in section 5.2 in a practical context. For an example, the case of packaging waste management has been chosen and reference is made to the lessons as described in section 5.3. This section should be considered as a pilot study aimed at reflecting upon operational aspects of economic instruments. It is not meant to provide guidelines for general applicability.

A brief introduction of the packaging waste problem, and of adopted policy approaches and instruments precede the analysis.

5.4.2 Packaging waste problems and current policy instruments

Packaging has important environmental aspects. OECD countries produced over 400 million tons of municipal waste annually in the late 1980s. Packaging generally comprises one-quarter to one-half of the municipal waste volume.

Environmental impacts of packaging include the use of scarce space when landfilled as waste, and the problem of litter in its stage of disposal, and air pollution as well as water pollution and generation of waste in its stage of production.

Measures to reduce the amount and toxicity of packaging and to encourage its recycling are currently being considered in at least 18 OECD countries [McCarthy, (1991)]. Objectives of waste management policies in these countries encompass:

a) A reduction of the waste volume and prevention of waste;
b) An increase in re-use and recycling;
c) Energy recovery through incineration;
d) A reduction of the amounts of waste incinerated and landfilled.

Policies that are currently being tried to reduce the packaging waste problem have at least three principles in common. First, a sharing of responsibility for managing packaging between government and the private sector is attempted through a wide range of measures, *e.g.*, establishing covenants with quantitative policy targets. Second, re-use and recycling of packaging materials are widely stimulated. Third, some countries apply bans on certain materials used in packaging manufacturing (heavy metals, PVC), or on certain types of packaging (cans for beer and soft drinks).

---

2. Parts of this section are based on Vos, in OECD (1993).

Economic instruments currently employed in packaging waste management have been listed in chapter 3. They include product charges and deposit-refund systems. Other instruments like waste-end charges and virgin materials charges may have an indirect impact on packaging waste.

5.4.3   *Packaging and policy instruments: operational analysis*

In section 5.2 a decision analysis framework for applicability of types of policy instruments to environmental problems has been described. This section is devoted to a concise evaluation of the use of such an approach to the packaging waste problem. We will apply the sequence of analyses as suggested in section 5.2 although restricting the analysis to two of the three stages mentioned, notably:

a) An analysis of conditions external to the choice of instrument problem and an analysis of possible, mainly pollution-related, characteristics which might be unconditional with respect to the choice of instruments.

b) A general analysis of the problem for which an adequate instrument must be chosen, and a suggestion with respect to broad types of instruments which could be considered feasible.

5.4.4   *External elements and strict conditions (stage 1)*

A first observation which must be made is that the packaging waste problem is a diffuse problem in terms of many applications and functions of packaging. Packaging is always related to one product or another, and the types of packaging as well as relevant conditions are as diverse as the products they "serve". Dependent on its function, packaging may be either indispensable (liquid or hazardous substances) or superfluous (double packaging of consumer products). Packaging waste might be either harmless (paper bag) or dangerous (empty pesticides containers). Also, packaging might be re-usable (glass bottles) or typically unique (packaging of meat-products). Hence, a once-and-for-all analysis cannot be made.

Some strong specific aspects which may dictate the choice of instruments have been mentioned in section 5.2. They include harmful impacts, short-term problems and great risks and uncertainties. One example concerns packaging of specified dangerous substances that are controlled by international direct legislation, for which international agreements may exist (*e.g.*, the EC Directive on Packaging of Hazardous Substances). Obviously, neither financial instruments nor social instruments are feasible alternatives. Another example relates to polystyrene packaging of food-stuffs and durable consumer products, for which CFCs were used. International agreements (Montreal, Copenhagen) will result in a short-term phase-out of the use of CFCs for this application. Here, the three conditions mentioned (harmfulness, short-term problems, uncertainty about impact) are fulfilled and direct regulation is a pre-eminent instrument.

For other types of packaging overriding conditions like the ones mentioned do not apply. These include, *inter alia*, primary packaging of consumer goods, beverages and food-stuff, and secondary packaging like shopping bags and cartons. We will restrict our analysis to such types.

A number of conditions external to the packaging waste management problem might also restrict the choice of instruments. We will preliminarily check factors suggested in section 5.2: i) international policy, ii) economic policy, including fiscal policy, and iii) other sectoral policies.

124

With regard to *international policy*, major impediments to the application of charges are formulated in the framework of the GATT, and in the Single European Act which are valid for the Member States of the EC. The GATT rules out all charges imposed on foreign products whilst domestic products are exempted. Also differences in charge rates between domestic and foreign products are forbidden. Next to these rules, the Single European Act prohibits discriminating taxation, for instance taxation of products which are hardly or not at all produced domestically, and for which non-charged domestic alternatives exist. Moreover, a ban on border control will be in place after completion of the EC-Internal Market, which will prevent the introduction of charges for reasons of enforceability. These conditions apply for all charges, including product charges on packaging.

Mandatory deposit-refund systems favour domestic producers which may lead to complaints about distortion of competition by foreign parties. Possible marketable permits exceeding national boundaries might be subject to so many rules agreed on by the parties concerned, that they will hardly be enforceable.

Economic policy is at stake if new products or structures would be enforced by regulation, that cost substantially more that traditional policy. Examples are mandatory deposit-refund systems, and take back responsibility for packaging producers. *Fiscal policy* might restrict the applicability of charges. Charges should be considered as elements in the fiscal system and should be judged against the background of fiscal legislation, which is well-developed and strict in many countries. Being a tax in a fiscal sense can be decisive for the way charges must be operated. It might be imperative to regulate in laws the charge basis, charge rates and liable groups. This may substantially decrease the flexibility of the charge system.

Other sectoral policies do not seem to impose heavy restrictions to the application of economic instruments to packaging. Of course, in balancing pros and cons of deposit-refund systems, additional transport and energy costs should not be overlooked.

5.4.5 Analysis of context of application (stage 2)

Restricting the analysis to the three main system characteristics mentioned in section 5.2 would have the following results:

Possibility for monitoring environmental impact of packaging waste is low since virtually everyone produces such waste which appears as part of waste bin contents or as litter, scattered throughout the economy. Accordingly, the *number of sources* is very high. The *costs for target groups* to reduce packaging waste are difficult to assess, but if we assume that, up to a certain level of recycling, they are relatively low, the packaging waste problem could be characterized as a policy situation like the "litter in natural areas" case described in section 5.2. It was suggested that such a problem can best be tackled through application of social instruments like information (eco-labelling), education and covenants. According to this analysis, economic instruments do not appear to be preferable.

The approach followed, however, ignores possibilities of "remote control" of the packaging waste problem. Although for the greater part the packaging waste problem is caused by consumers, also other parties could be taken as the main target groups of the instruments to be operated. Authorities in many countries seek to shift (part of the) responsibility for the packaging waste problem to those who produce, distribute and use it. A clear example can be found in the German *Verpackungsverordnung*. If producers and distributors are made responsible, policy instruments could also be aimed at these target groups. Hence, the analysis of system characteristics changes considerably.

Possibility for monitoring has become a meaningless criterium, but *accessibility of polluting activities* has been formulated as an alternative main situation characteristic. Accessibility could be rated high, since the packaging industry is a rather well-organised branch of industry. The *number of sources* is relatively low as a result of considerable concentrations in the packaging industry. *Costs of compliance* depend on available solutions which probably are as manifold as applications of packaging. Would they be high, and probably largely variable for that reason, we find a policy situation, for which developing economic instruments could be an advisable approach. Low costs of compliance result in a policy situation in which direct regulation could be prominent among the alternative options.

5.5 Some Conclusions

a)   The approach presented in this chapter offers an interesting view on a rather complicated matter. Although the approach is rather rough, it adds a number of valuable thoughts to operational instruments analysis. This does not, however, alter the fact that in specific cases, in-depth analysis is needed for a balanced choice of instruments. The approach serves to arrive at first approximations of which type of instrument might work well (on *a priori* grounds) in certain contexts of application. Fine-tuning and mixing of instruments has to be done subsequently.

b)   The complexity of instrument choice points at the necessity of a multi-stage approach in which case studies should follow after analysis of a more general character.

c)   When referring to the set of criteria for evaluation of the choice of instruments, the focus is on environmental effectiveness, on economic efficiency, and on acceptability. Practical characteristics of contexts of application for policy instruments can act as indications for types of instruments that should be further examined on a detailed level.

d)   A distinction between source-related and pollution-impact related characteristics is useful. It appears that source-related characteristics are dominant in guiding the choice of instruments, whereas impact-related characteristics might unconditionally restrict the set of instruments to choose between in specific situations.

References

BOVENBERG A.L. *et al.* (1992), *Instrumentkeuze in het Milieubeleid* (Choice of Instruments in Environmental Policy), Discussion Paper no. 9102, Dutch Ministry for Economic Affairs.

CANADIAN GOVERNMENT (1992), *Economic Instruments for Environmental Protection: Discussion Paper*, Ottawa.

LAVE L. and GRUENSPECHT H. (1991), "Increasing the Efficiency and Effectiveness of Environmental Decisions: Benefit-Cost Analysis and Effluent Fees", in, J. Air Waste Manage. Assoc. vol. 41, no. 5, pp 680-693.

MACCARTHY J. (1992), *Reduction and Recycling of Packaging Waste*, Environment Monograph N° 62, OECD, Paris.

OECD (1991), *Environmental Policy: How to Apply Economic Instruments*, OECD, Paris.

OPSCHOOR J.B. and D.W. PEARCE (1991), (eds) *Persistent Pollutants*, Dordrecht.

STAVINS R.N. (1990), "Innovative Policies for Sustainable Development in the 1990's: Economic Incentives for Environmental Protection," Paper prepared for the UNECE, Washington D.C.

TIETENBERG T. (1992), "Relevant Experiences with Tradeable Entitlements," in, *Combating Global Warming*, UNCTAD, New York.

VOS J.B. (1993), "Applying Economic Instruments to Packaging Waste: Practical Issues for Product Charges and Deposit Refund Systems", OECD Environment monograph No.82, OECD Paris.

VOS J.B. *et al.* (1992), *Buitenlandse Ervaringen met Financiële Instrumenten voor het Milieubeleid*, (Foreign Experiences with Financial Instruments for Environmental Policy), Report to the Dutch Ministry for the Environment, IVM/DHV, Amsterdam/Amersfoort.

Wetenschappelijke Raad voor het Regeringsbeleid (Scientific Council for Government Policy) (1992), *Milieubeleid: Stategie, Instrumenten en Handhaafbaarheid* (Environmental Policy: Strategy, Instruments and Enforceability), The Hague.

Chapter 6

Taxation and Environment in European Economies in Transition

The formerly planned economies in Europe are presently in a process of transition to some type of market economy. Processes of restructuring are under way, each country following its own path, but all aspiring to improve the efficiency of their economies by increasing the role of market forces. The transition process is economically painful requiring substantial short term sacrifices, in terms of production backdrops and unemployment.

The poor state of the environment in these countries is well documented. Compared to OECD member states with market economies, the planned economies had a high use of primary resources per unit of final product, resulting in a high level of environmentally damaging emissions. The political and economic causes for the relative neglect of environmental problems that has been a feature of the planned economies are analyzed in Godard [in OECD (1994)]. Economies in transition are faced with a double task. Improving the efficiency of their production systems, as well as dealing with the adverse environmental legacy of the period of the planned economy.

One of the elements of economic restructuring is the creation of a tax system that is adapted to the new role of the state in society and to the needs of a market economy.
The simultaneous need for ecological improvement and fiscal reform raises the question whether, and if so in what manner, these tasks can be combined. This has been the subject of an OECD-workshop (Paris, February 25-26 1993), at which papers were presented about the general subject of taxation and environment in economies in transition, and about the state of affairs in some of the countries involved.

Section 6.1 sets out the main issues, borrowing strongly from Godard [in OECD (1994)] and the draft summary of the discussions in the workshop. Sections 6.2 to 6.7 survey the present state of affairs concerning environmental charges and taxes in Russia, Estonia, Poland, Hungary and Czechoslovakia.

The discussion in this chapter concerns only charges and taxes. This is not to rule out the potential usefulness of deposit refunds, an instrument used also in the period of the planned economy. Zylicz (1992) contains a moderate plea for tradeable permits, on the grounds of the certainty offered by the pollution ceiling, but granting that actual trading activity would presumably be limited.

6.1 Taxation and environment in economies in transition: the main issues

The following issues figure prominently in the debate about taxation and environment in economies in transition:

a) The effectiveness of incentive charges in the transition phase.

In planned economies enterprises, not in the least those in the manufacturing sector with high pollution intensity, were not subject to competition and faced soft budget constraints. In the transition phase there is a carry-over from this period, as market oriented management behaviour and new market relationships are not established overnight and (semi-)monopolies still prevail. Therefore it is conceivable that environmental charges, even if the rates are substantial, will simply be included in cost and passed on in product prices without modification of pollution behaviour. Environmental taxes would, in this situation, raise substantial revenues without achieving any environmental goals.

Management is not accustomed to facing choices as to production technology. Knowledge about technologies for pollution abatement is especially bad, as due to the weak enforcement of environmental policies in these countries no sector producing pollution control equipment has evolved.

Hyper inflation, a phenomenon that is quite common in economies in transition, may erode real charge rates and render incentive effects illusionary.

So are incentive charges necessarily ineffective? Not necessarily. First it should be noted that the strength of the argument for ineffectiveness is contingent. The countries involved differ substantially in the sectoral coverage, and speed of their privatisation programmes. Some countries are already quite far ahead in privatisation, whilst in others the manufacturing sector is still dominated by public enterprises.

Second, it can be argued that during the period of transition decision-makers in enterprises will have to come to terms with new constraints, and new procedures for making decisions. During this period they may be more sensitive to the financial incentives provided by environmental taxes than they would be at a later time, when enterprise management settles down to a matter of routine.

Third, knowledge about pollution control technologies can be actively disseminated by environmental authorities among polluting enterprises. According to Huppes and Kagan (1989) the active dissemination of knowledge about pollution control technology by environmental authorities themselves has contributed to the incentive effect of the Dutch water pollution charge.

The problem of non-availability of pollution control equipment can be addressed by technology transfers from OECD-countries. Hyper inflation can be addressed by indexing charge rates. Poland has made an attempt at indexation, that has been just partially successful. The practical problems of designing an effective and politically acceptable index mechanism deserve strong attention.

b) Shortage of administrative resources

Both tax policies and environmental policies have to be operated in the face of shortages of administrative resources of adequate calibre. This implies that tax approaches to environmental policy may be most attractive where they reduce the requirements for administrative resources. In practice, monitoring and enforcement of the complex emission charge systems that are in existence is weak. This suggests that introducing environmental incentives into taxes which have to be levied anyway (e.g., taxes on goods and services) may be a way of making the most of limited administrative resources.

The shortage of financial/accountancy skills required in tax administration should rule out the introduction of complex schemes of environmental tax differentiation. Protection of essential fiscal revenues in transition economies requires that tax systems should be designed to be simple and easily enforced. Complexity and sophistication could imply use of resources that would be better employed on basic administration and enforcement activities.

c) Economic and political impacts of incentive charges.

Incentive charges impose two types of burdens on polluting enterprises. These are, the cost of pollution control itself and the charge on non-abated emissions. This may result in additional bankruptcies of pollution intensive industries, possibly thwarting the socio-political acceptability of the transition process in which economic hardships are already involved. Polluting industries generally oppose charges as a "double burden", preferring a policy of direct regulation over which they expect to have more control. Strong industry resistance against incentive charges is a general feature of OECD policy experience. In view of this, and in agreement with OECD-guidelines on the application of economic instruments, the socio-political acceptability of charges is an urgent point. The problem of acceptability can be addressed by:

- Advance announcement - The acceptability of the German water pollution charge has been improved by advance announcement, enabling industry to invest timely in pollution control equipment [OECD (1989)];

- Stepwise rate rises - Charge rates can be increased progressively, either according to a prefixed schedule or learning from experience on the basis of perceived incentive effects;

- Consultation procedures - Consultation of industry can promote acceptance and improve the practical design of the charge. It can also empower industry, by providing knowledge about pollution control technology;

- Subsidising pollution control - The charge rate can be set below the optimal incentive level, using the revenue to subsidize pollution control investments. In theory [Pezzey (1988)], a charge-subsidy can achieve the same environmental effects as a charge at the Pigovian rate. In practice this result depends on the proper design of the subsidy scheme, which is not a simple matter;

- Rebating charge revenue - If charge revenues are rebated fully to polluters independent of polluters' control behaviour (e.g., a lump sum), the cost-effectiveness property is retained while the transfer element is eliminated. For instance, with the Swedish NO_x charge revenue is rebated to polluters on the basis of their production;

- Exempting pollution-intensive industries - While this solution appears to be politically expedient, it may detract strongly from environmental and cost effectiveness and can be called into question on equity grounds. Cost effectiveness is impaired definitely, if the marginal control costs of pollution intensive industry happen to be sloping upward steeply.

As a final note, it should be borne in mind that, assuming part of the burden will inevitably be shifted to firms, any newly imposed tax, whether environmental or not, puts a burden on the economy. The specific feature of environmental charges is that the burden is stronger on pollution intensive industries.

d) Financing environmental expenditure

Presently economies in transition operate "environmental funds" (*cf.* sections 6.2 to 6.7) that finance a broad range of environmental expenditure. These funds are fed by the revenue of emission charges and non-compliance fees. The question arises whether this practice of earmarking, that predates the recent economic/political changes, should be continued.

Earmarking revenues from environmental taxes and charges has been common practice in many OECD economies, and may appear to have attractions to policy-makers in transition economies. In general, earmarking carries significant risks of decision-making inefficiency in the public sector. It provides the agency receiving the tax revenues with a privileged budgetary status, which may result in resources being used in the agency which would be of more value elsewhere in the government budget. Earmarking could be acceptable as a transition measure. In transition economies environmental expenditures will probably contribute not more than 1 per cent-2 per cent of GDP in the next couple of years. Thus the risk of inefficiency conventionally associated with earmarked funds is constrained by the absolute level of spending, and it could be deemed of minor importance when confronted with the risks from letting the environment compete with short-term political priorities reflected in budgetary debates.

A problem with earmarking is that hyper inflation erodes revenues, if charge rates are not indexed in a satisfactory manner. This problem is less important with general taxation on labour incomes or goods, of which revenue rises correspondingly to increases in the general price level.

e) Timing: should environmental taxes be introduced in the transition phase or at a later stage?

Economies in transition are in the process of rebuilding their tax systems. New taxes have to be introduced, to raise revenue and to replace old taxes that are not in line with the demands of a market economy. So there appears to be a unique opportunity now to introduce environmental taxes. A restructuring of the tax system, levying environmental taxes and decreasing general taxation, at a later stage may be more difficult once the tax system has taken a definitive shape and fiscal bureaucracies and societal interest groups have taken a vested interest in it. The strength of this "now or never" argument depends critically on the administrative resources available to devise and implement here and now a set of environmental charges that fulfil a number of minimum requirements with regard to:

- implementability, with the limited administrative resources available;
- revenue predictability and stability - There should be reasonable estimates of initial revenue and charge elasticities;
- EC concordance - As EC membership is aspired by many economies in transition, it would be unwise to design a product tax system that is fundamentally different from EC-member states.

These conditions appear to be fulfilled rather well by taxes on energy products, car petrol in particular. Energy taxes are cheap and easy to collect and enforce, and can contribute substantial resources. Many of the problems of increasing or restructuring energy taxes in OECD countries have to do with the disruption this may cause to existing patterns of competition. Introducing such taxes during a period when substantial restructuring is already taking place may be better than introducing high energy taxes later, when a second round of adjustment would be required.

f) Dealing with legacies of the planned economy.

Sections 6.2 to 6.7 document the present state of affairs concerning environmental charges, subsidies and primary resource prices, that is largely inherited from the period of the planned economy. One way of dealing practically with the interrelationship between environment and taxation is to focus first on existing practices that are detrimental from the viewpoint of an effective and efficient environmental policy.

Some of the elements that deserve reconsideration are:

- differential charge rates for different polluters - Various existing environmental charges have rates that differ per economic sector. Generally speaking, rates for households are lowest and rates for heavy industry are highest. In Russia local authorities implementing charges can discretionarily grant exemptions, on grounds that have nothing to do with environmental effects. These practices are not warranted from an efficiency point of view.

- Earmarking revenue of non-compliance fees - Environmental funds are generally fed with revenue from non-compliance fees. This practice provides agencies managing the funds with the perverse incentive of continuing non-compliance practices.

- Subsidies on energy products - In some countries prices of energy products are subsidized, a practice constituting an obvious environmental disincentive. Furthermore, this is in total disagreement with existing energy excises in OECD-countries, especially in the EC.

- Administrative prices for primary resources - One legacy from the period of the planned economy, that appears to be continued at least in some countries, is artificially low prices for primary resources. Establishing conditions that lead to market pricing for primary resources would eliminate an environmental disincentive.

- Tax expenditures - Some countries provide environmental subsidies indirectly by tax expenditures. The disadvantage is that the level of the subsidy is less clear than if it is paid directly. Furthermore, in view of the acute revenue shortages in most transition economies, it is particularly important that environmental tax prices should not be introduced in a way which squanders scarce tax revenues.

6.2 The case of the Russian Federation

a) Three categories of tax revenue can be distinguished:

	Revenue (billion rbl in 1992)
• General taxation: VAT, corporate profits tax, excises, provisions for price regulation fund, property tax	3157
• Taxes and contributions related to the environment:	
-- Payments for natural resource use rights	101
-- Contributions for mineral resources exploration	68
-- Land tax	33
-- Forestry levy	14
-- Payments for industrial water consumption	10
	226
• Pollution charges	
-- Air pollution	2
-- Water pollution	4
-- Waste disposal	1
	7
Total	**3390**

b) General taxation consists mainly of indirect taxes.

c) The second category of taxes can be regarded as "environmental" to a limited extent:

-- For administrative simplicity payments for natural resource use rights are on (net) production, not on (gross) resource use. So there is no incentive to avoid losses in production.

-- Contributions for mineral resource exploration and prospecting have been traditionally used to finance mineral resources research and inspection activities.

-- The land tax is levied on non-agricultural land usage, with revenues earmarked for land use, land protection and infrastructure.

-- Revenue of the forestry levy is for subsidizing forest reproduction.

-- Payments for industrial water consumption finance water distribution, reproduction and sewage facilities. Agricultural enterprises are exempted.

6.2.1   Primary resource prices

In the centrally planned economies prices of primary resources were very low compared to prices of final products. This induced over utilization of primary resources, with negative environmental impacts. Price liberalization has not changed much the relationship between prices of primary resources and final products, which still diverge from world market conditions due to the continuing existence of quasi-monopolies in product markets and the high level of indirect taxes. This remains a serious obstacle to a rational and environmentally responsible use of primary resources.

6.2.2 Emission charges

Charges on air pollution, water pollution and waste disposal have two rates, one for emissions allowed within the permit, and non-compliance fees for emissions above the permitted level. Charges are paid out of profits net of other taxes. Charge rates are differentiated per substance, dependent on the degree of toxicity that is administratively set at the quotient of actual emissions and emissions allowed in the permit. There are "correction coefficients" to take into account the local environmental and socio-economic situation. Correction coefficients are determined by local authorities on the basis of centrally determined guidelines (usually as maximum/minimum figures). Local authorities also have the discretion to apply exemptions, dependent on socio-economic factors and the degree of pollution abatement undertaken by the polluter. Charge revenues are for state non-budget ecological funds (90 per cent) and the federal budget (10 per cent).

It appears that local authorities amply use their discretion in applying correction coefficients and exemptions for specific polluters. Also polluters simply refuse to pay. The centrally determined, rate structure is complex, distinguishing 300 substances in air pollution and 150 substances in water pollution, but according to Gofman and Gusev in [OECD (1994)] "actual measurement of emissions scarcely takes place". Incentive effects are doubtful anyhow in view of the low level of charge rates.

Real charge rates are undermined by galloping inflation rates. Rates have been raised by 500 per cent in 1992, but this may not have been sufficient to keep real rates constant.

6.2.3 Future developments

For 1993 a restructuring of the entire tax system is envisaged. This includes the introduction of an energy tax, simultaneously reducing VAT on energy products to the same extent.

In the document proposing the new tax system an intention is expressed to increase the incentive function of pollution charges and to apply indexation to pollution charge rates. The progressiveness of the charge structure, with higher rates for emissions above the permitted level, is to be strongly stepped up. State authorities will have the discretion to (temporarily or permanently) close down producers that have insufficient profits to pay the charges for emissions above the permitted level. On the other hand, charges for emissions below the permit level will be fiscally deductible.

6.3 The case of Estonia

The structure of environmental charges in Estonia bears resemblance to the Russian situation.

6.3.1 Emission charges

Charges for emissions to air and water and for waste disposal exist for up to 50 pollutants, the rates varying by toxicity (measured as the quotient of actual and officially permitted emissions). Local correction coefficients can be applied at the discretion of local authorities. Charge bills are based on input resource characteristics and stack gas volume. Exemptions can be granted in case of abatement efforts by the polluter. In 1991 emission charges provided 91 per cent of the revenue of the "Estonian Environmental Fund", which is also fed by non-compliance fees in water and air pollution. Charge rates are determined by budgetary needs, *i.e.*, planned expenditures of the Fund. Fund revenues have rapidly increased in 1991, but are constantly eroded by high inflation rates. No indexation of charge rates has taken place. Charge rates are insufficient for incentive effects. Due to "soft budget constraints" in many industrial enterprises, that carried over their monopolistic status from the old regime, incentive effects are hard to achieve anyhow [Kallaste in OECD (1994)].

6.3.2   *User charges*

User charges are levied for water treatment and waste collection and treatment, with revenues going to local authorities. Resource payments are due for land use, use of water, oil shale, peat, etc. Since 1991 these are based on available resources, not on produced resources, so there is an incentive to encourage efficiency in extraction.

6.3.3   *Deposit refunds*

Traditionally there is a deposit refund on glass bottles, functioning poorly due to insufficient return outlets. A restructuring of the system is envisaged.

6.4   The case of Poland

Poland has an extensive system of emission charges and non-compliance fees. There are no environmental charges on products. A proposal for a 4 per cent fuel charge (*ad valorem*) has been rejected by Parliament. Generally, in Poland there is much resistance against, and little understanding of, product charges [Zylicz, in OECD (1994)].

6.4.1   *Emission charges*

There is a fee on emissions of waste water and saline water, based on BOD, COD, suspended solids (US$ 64/ton), chlorate and sulphate ions (US$ 5/ton), heavy metals (US$ 7407/ton) and volatile phenols (US$ 2963/ton). BOD and COD rates are differentiated per economic sector. The BOD rate varies from US$ 129 for rural municipal sewage, hospitals and social care institutions to US$ 1489/ton for power generation, fuel processing, chemical, metallurgical, machine and light industries. The COD rate varies from US$ 77 to US$ 1027/ton.

A fee is levied on emissions of atmospheric pollutants, the rate structure distinguishing 12 groups of pollutants. Both the waste water and the air pollution fee are the same for all administrative regions, except for Katowice and Krakow where double rates apply. The charge rate for SO_2 is US$ 80/ton, for hydrocarbons it is US$ 222/ton, for particulate matter US$ 44-222/ton. For "strongly toxic" emissions (*e.g.*, benzene and chromium) a rate of US$ 74074 applies, for "toxic" emissions (dioxin and cadmium) a rate of US$ 37037. The waste disposal fee distinguishes four categories of waste, depending on toxicity, with rates increasing from US$ 1.48/ton for non-toxic waste to US$ 18.52/ton for strongly toxic waste.

The fee structure, especially for air pollution, is rather complicated, even more so if one takes actual limited monitoring capacity into account. Nevertheless, the fact that a fee is levied does contain an implicit incentive for inspecting agencies to step up monitoring activity.

6.4.2   Non-compliance fees

Non-compliance fees are assessed for all pollutants for which regular emission charges are collected, and also for noise. Generally rates are much higher than emission charge rates. For instance, non-compliance fees in air pollution are ten times the emission fee.

In case of non-compliance lasting for more than three years, fee rates are doubled. Fee revenues are for the National Fund for Environmental Protection and Water Resource Management (around 40 per cent), and its 49 regional counterparts administered by regional administrators (around 60 per cent). Fee revenues account for 40 per cent of total environmental expenditure, which is presently at around 1.0 per cent of GDP.

6.4.3   User charges

User charges are levied on abstractions of surface water and groundwater, differentiated to economic sectors and differing per administrative region. There is a locally administered fee for tree removal.

Mining extraction fees are based on the price of extracted minerals.

6.4.4   Tax allowances

There is an extensive system of tax allowances, exempting pollution abatement equipment and recycled goods from the sales tax and allowing fiscal deductibility of environmental investments by farmers.

6.4.5   Future developments

It is expected that rates of emission fees will be stabilized (in real terms), for economic reasons. Locally administrated user fees for environment-related services (waste collection, sewage treatment, etc.) may rise as subsidies are abolished. These services may be privatized. There is a tendency to increase the share of the revenue going to regional authorities from emission fees and non compliance fees.

6.4.6   Evaluation

The extensive fee system has evolved in Poland since the 1970's. Recently, there have been some reforms and a proposal has been accepted to index charge rates to the inflation rate.

Data about practical administration, actual measurement of emissions and enforcement of the fees are lacking. The fee system "starts to bring positive results" [Zylicz, in OECD (1994)], as fee rates have been increased and economic reforms have increased polluter's incentives to save on costs. However it is difficult to identify the effect of the fee system separately, as at the same time enforcement activities have been stepped up, subsidies from the National Fund have increased and the economic reforms themselves have forced some of the most polluting industries to close down. On the other hand tax allowances have been decreased.

Although fee rates have been raised, they are still substantially below Pigouvian levels. Rates are barely differentiated according to spatial factors, due to constitutional limitations on allowable regional tax differentiation.

There is an excessive differentiation for equity reasons, with high rates for manufacturing industry and low rates for households and government institutions. In net terms the environmental funds have acted as agencies transferring resources from manufacturing industries to municipalities, thus reinforcing wrong signals sent to the household sector.

6.5 The case of the Czech and Slovak Republics

The assessment presented below is based on the situation in 1992, before the formal defederalization of Czechoslovakia.

6.5.1 *Emission charges*

In the Czech Republic air pollution charges are levied on emissions of, solids, SO_2, NO_x, CO and C_xH_y. In koruny per metric ton base rates are 3000, 1000, 800, 600 and 2000 respectively. In cases of proven abatement projects 40 per cent of the charge is deferred during the project. In addition nearly 90 other harmful substances are listed, divided into three classes, with rates ranging from koruny 1,000 to 20,000 per metric ton. Air pollution charges will be increased gradually, from 30 per cent of the full rate in 1992, to 100 per cent in 1997.

Water effluent charges have two components. The base rate is determined by the costs of generally applicable methods of treatment of waste water. The surcharge depends on damage inflicted to water quality. Original 1989 rates have been doubled in 1992. The charge base includes BSK5, undissolved substances, crude oil substances, evident alkalinity and acidity and dissolved organic salts.
In the Czech Republic charges for waste storage depend on the quantity and category of stored waste. If the dump complies to regulations for operating dumps, the base rate applies with revenue going to the community in which the dump is located. If the dump does not comply, the operator pays a non compliance fee at a higher rate per ton of waste disposed.

6.5.2 *Non-compliance fees*

For air pollution, polluters pay a 50 per cent surcharge on the base rates of regular emission charges for emissions above permitted levels.

In waste disposal, if a dump does not comply to environmental regulations a non-compliance fee is levied with revenue flowing into the State environment fund. In 1997 all dumps will have to comply. Dependent on the type of waste, the high rate exceeds the base rate by 0 to 1200 per cent (for hazardous waste). The high rate is to be greatly increased, the increase varying between 67 per cent and 1000 per cent, from 1992 until 1994.

Non-compliance fees have recently been increased, up to a maximum of 10 million koruny.

There are no data on monitoring and enforcement of charge systems. Together, emission charges and non-compliance fees are the main revenues of the State environment funds in the Czech and Slovak

Republic, providing finance for various types of environmental programs. Other revenues include allocations from State budgets, donations from domestic and foreign donors, etc.

6.5.3   *Future developments*

In 1993 a new taxation system is to come into effect in the Czech and Slovak Republics containing a strong environmental component:

-- The reduced VAT rate (5 per cent in stead of 23 per cent) will apply to environmentally sound products, *e.g.*, water soluble paints, recycled paper, thermal pumps, passenger electrocars and biogas.
-- For the excise duty a reduced rate is envisaged for lead free petrol, and exemptions for bionaphta and biogas. Vehicles with catalytic converters will be exempt from the road tax.
-- Income and corporation tax exempts incomes from small hydroelectric power (up to 1 MW), wind power, solar energy, biogas production, geothermal energy, thermal pumps and equipment for production of bio-degradable substances.
-- Up to a limit, donations for ecological purposes will be fiscally deductible.
-- Charge payments according to base rates for air and water pollution and waste storage will be fiscally deductible. Surcharges are to be paid out of net profits.

Ecological ministries of the republics are considering:

-- Product taxes on ozone depleting substances, pesticides, fertilizer, asbestos and selected types of paints.
-- Taxes on raw materials, such as coal, gravel sands, industrial sands and limestone.
-- Tax on water consumption, form surface and ground water.
-- Tax on mineral resource extraction.
-- Tax on noise.

6.6   The case of Hungary

6.6.1   *Product charges*

A product charge of around 0.7 per cent of market price is levied on motor vehicle fuels since May 1st 1992. Revenue goes to the Central Environmental Fund, with most of it earmarked for environmental expenditure relating to vehicle traffic. The remainder is earmarked for other purposes such as nature conservation and raising environmental awareness.

The tax on petrol is lower for the lead-free variety, approximately equalizing market prices including taxes.

The consumption tax for new cars provided with a catalytic converter has a discount of Forint 50,000.

6.6.2   Non-compliance fees

There is an extensive system of "environment protection penalties". The penalties are levied when emissions exceed a pre specified emission standard. Rates are differentiated per pollutant(3), depending on rate of toxicity and/or degree of environmental damage inflicted. Data about actual measurements are lacking. The penalties are proportional to emissions above the emission standard. Penalties are levied for waste water, drainage, air pollution, hazardous waste and noise and vibration. Revenue is for the Central Environment Protection Fund.

6.6.3   Tax allowances

There is a corporate tax allowance of 40 per cent for investments in emission abatement equipment in the environmental compartments of air, water and hazardous waste. Also equipment for environmental protection is liable for accelerated depreciation (in 3 years).

There is a tax allowance for joint ventures (foreign capital) producing equipment for environmental protection. The allowance is at 100 per cent for the first five years and 60 per cent for a further five years if foreign capital participation exceeds 30 per cent, the investment exceeds 50 million forint and more than 50 per cent of company income is from environmental protection equipment. Since 1992, no new applications can be made to this scheme.

6.6.4   Deposit refunds

Deposit fees are levied for glass bottles.

---

3.   For instance, for the air pollution penalty 300 pollutants are distinguished.

Data Sources

The sections on Russia, Poland, Estonia and Hungary derive their data from papers, prepared for the OECD-workshop on "Taxation and Environment in European Economies in Transition", Paris February 25-26, 1993 and published in "Taxation and Environment in Economies in Transition" OECD, Paris 1994.

Data for the section on Czechoslovakia are from: "Czechoslovakia: Economics and the Environment", Report transmitted by the delegation of Czechoslovakia to the Joint Working Group on Environment and Economics, Economic Commission for Europe to the Economic and Social Council of the UN (November 1992).

References

GODARD (1994), "Conditions for and obstacles to the introduction of tax instruments for environmental protection in European economies in transition" in "Taxation and Environment in Economies in Transition", OECD, Paris, 1994.

HUPPES G. and KAGAN R.A. (1989), "Market-oriented regulation of environmental problems in the Netherlands", *Law and Policy*, April.

PEZZEY J. (1988), "Market mechanisms of pollution control: 'Polluter Pays', economic and practical aspects", in, R.K. Turner (ed.), *Sustainable Environmental Management*, Boulder (Co).

WEITZMAN M.L. (1992), "Prices vs. Quantities", *Review of Economic Studies*, October, pp 683-691.

ZYLICZ T. (1992), "Implementing environmental policies in Central and Eastern Europe", paper presented to the second meeting of the International Society for Ecological Economics, Stockholm August 3-6.

PART III

INTERNATIONAL ASPECTS

Chapter 7

Economic Instruments for Global Environmental Problems

7.1 Backgrounds

Environmental problems manifest themselves at a range of spatial levels - local, regional, continental, global. Once environmental degradation crosses national borders, they potentially give rise to special policy problems. There generally is no administrative superstructure that can, with sovereignty, deal with them. At worst, this takes us into the realm of prisoners' dilemmas and tragedies of the commons (see chapter 2), with the problem remaining unresolved. At best, countries on their own accord unilaterally reduce transboundary environmental degradation. In reality countries find themselves somewhere in between, in the realm of international negotiation.

In this chapter the focus will be on global environmental issues and policy instruments to address these issues. Examples of global issues include global warming, biodiversity loss, stratospheric ozone depletion. Some attention will also be paid to other transboundary problems.

Global environmental issues arise when processes operative in the earth's biosphere transport and transform environmental degradation into a problem in which a large number of countries have a stake. They are the results of actions in individual countries but the welfare of other countries is potentially or actually adversely affected. In the absence of a global environmental regulator, international coordination through voluntary agreements is required.

Not only can one discern a growing activity in this field as witnessed by the emergence of conventions on several global issues, but there is also a growing interest in using economic instruments in implementing such agreements [see, *e.g.*, OECD (1991d); UNCED (1992)].

A distinction must be made between instruments used at the international/global level, and lower (national) level instruments directed at global issues. Examples of the latter are the carbon charges that were reported on in chapter 4. These are national charges but they are officially motivated by the climate issue and are calculated with reference to the carbon content of products. In this chapter we are primarily concerned with instruments to be applied within the context of international agreements. OECD has recently published two important volumes on the implementation of two particularly interesting economic instruments in policies directed at climate change, one on a tradeable permit system [OECD (1992e)] and the other on a tax system (OECD (1992f) and (1993b)].

In this chapter we present an overview of the issues and the options involved in policy development vis-a-vis global environmental issues. Most frequently, but for practical reasons only, reference will be to the climate change issue.

7.2 Principles for international environmental policies

Since the previous report on the use of economic instruments [OECD (1989)], the interest in global environmental issues has increasingly manifested itself. The Montreal Protocol became operational in 1987, and since then conventions and agreements have been concluded on Climate Change and Biodiversity (both signed at the UNCED Conference in 1992).

The main perimeters of international environmental policy in the decades ahead, have been set by the principles as laid down in the Rio Declaration on Environment and Development [UN (1992)]. We refer especially to:

-- the sovereign right of states to exploit their own resources and the responsibility to ensure that activities within their jurisdiction do not cause damage to the environment of other states or of areas beyond the limits of national jurisdiction (Principle 2);

-- The duty to cooperate (with common, but differentiated responsibilities) to conserve, protect and restore the health and integrity of the Earth's ecosystems (Principle 7);

-- The application of "the precautionary approach" (Principle 15);

-- the promotion of the internalisation of environmental costs and the use of economic instruments, taking into account the approach that the polluter should, in principle, bear the cost of pollution (Principle 16).

Global problems often can only be addressed on the basis of international approaches but sometimes countries may not be prepared to take measures beyond what is justified on the basis of short term or purely national interests. The pursuit of widely endorsed objectives related to global issues will not automatically and immediately be embraced by all countries that are sources of pollutants relevant to these issues, or source-countries may not feel inclined to go along with international efforts to the desired goal. This leads to the well-known free rider issue, *i.e.*, some countries may reap benefits of others' environmental policies without contributing to that effort themselves. In as much as this is an impediment to reaching an optimal (or at least desirable) level of abatement activity in the views of other countries, the latter might propose to compensate in one way or another such reluctant countries to join in with collective efforts. Also, efficiency arguments might be raised in favour of some countries financing environmental measures in other countries, on the basis of differences in the relevant marginal abatement cost functions (the "joint implementation issue" that we shall come back to below).

The Montreal Protocol on the Protection of the Ozone layer and the Framework Convention on Climate Change both have financial mechanisms attached that facilitate compensations to be made by the developed and industrialised countries, to the developing countries. At present the "Global Environmental Facility" is set up to multilaterally manage such mechanisms and others that relate to several environmental problems with global significance. An example at the bilateral level is that of the "Debt-for-Nature" swaps whereby developed countries buy partly written off debts of developing countries to acquit the debtor countries in their local currency on the condition that certain environmental measures are taken by that country.

A distinction may exist between the relative degrees to which (groups of) countries suffer from transboundary or global environmental problems or give rise to these problems. Voluntary agreement between the source and receptor countries may then not easily come about. In such cases other principles such as the "victim pays principle" and the "reciprocal compensation principle" have been put forward in the academic literature. The first of these means that the country suffering from pollution pays for expenses to reduce pollution in the source country. The latter principle would be a mixed system of a pollution charge and a pollution abatement duty to be paid respectively by the polluting and the polluted country in the case of unidirectional externalities [Barde (1992), quoting Smets H. in OECD (1976)].

7.3 Strategies and instruments

7.3.1   Unidirectional and reciprocal externalities

Transboundary environmental issues are the results of actions in individual countries that adversely affect the welfare of other countries. Two types of international externalities have been discerned (chapter 2) -reciprocal externalities, where all countries contribute directly to the environmental problem, and unidirectional externalities, where some cause the externality and others undergo it. Sometimes reciprocal externalities are divided into regional ones and global ones [Mäler (1990)]. Unidirectional externalities cannot, strictly speaking, give rise to global environmental problems, but they may give rise to problems labelled to be "of global significance" that therefore merit multilateral attention.

In the case of significant international externalities, one possible approach is that some very concerned countries undertake unilateral action [see Hoel (1991) for some caveats in this respect], but normally to be effective, international coordination through agreements is required. Even so, countries might opt for not entering agreements to deal with the issue at hand and to become free riders, *i.e.*, they would not share in the costs of measures whilst enjoying the benefits of the collective efforts of the other countries. In the case of unidirectional externalities such free riding behaviour cannot be countered by others polluting more in order to punish the free rider [OECD (1991)]. Hence other forms of establishing reciprocity would have to come in force. Even in cases of reciprocal externalities, countries might decide to not participate in a collective effort, if their valuation of environmental quality is relatively low. In such cases, incentives may be needed to make such countries engage in the agreement such as the side payments already referred to in the previous section.

7.3.2   Strategies and instruments

In terms of ultimate environmental impact, there are several ways in which environmental policies could be effective.

One is, to relocate activities to areas where they will contribute less to the global issue at stake. This may be an appropriate avenue to consider in relation to problems such as biological diversity, but in cases such as the climate issue or the ozone problem, relocation does not provide the solution, since the environment is indifferent to the location of the source.

Environmental degradation can also be avoided by reducing source strengths through reduction of activity levels, diffusion of existing cleaner technology and/or innovation. Innovation could lead to credits that could have a value in cases where international action would reward the creation of such credits *e.g.*, by making them tradeable.

A final strategy is that of circumventing the environmental impact by enhancing the environment's capacity to absorb or otherwise deal with the pollution. Sink enhancement for example, through afforestation is one relatively inexpensive method of dealing with carbon dioxide emissions, the major greenhouse forcing agent. Depending on the value of the benefits and the costs of sink enhancement, this might therefore be a promising option to explore for some countries, especially when space is available for forests to be expanded.

There are several possible types of international instruments. So far, agreements and conventions on international environmental degradation have often sought consensus about national efforts in terms of target setting for emissions reduction. One can think of examples in the field of acidification (the SO2 reduction "clubs"), CFCs, climate change (carbon or energy use reduction targets). It would then be a matter to be dealt with at the national level, to decide how these reduction targets would translate into national policies and instruments. Global environmental issues will most probably not be efficiently dealt with if the international community were to rely only on pro rata agreed emissions reductions. Also, a recent OECD survey of prospective modelling results in the area of CO_2 reductions concluded that target setting which does not respect differences in abatement costs across sectors or countries "...is likely to be much more costly than targets which leave flexibility in abatement decisions. Gains due to flexibility in abatement increase disproportionately with the stringency of the target" [Hoeller *et al* (1992)].

Flexible approaches must be developed and this is where economic instruments may have a part to play, especially in reinforcing of more comprehensive strategies.

There are various types of economic instruments available for addressing global environmental issues:

a) Emissions charges or products charges or even combinations such as an international carbon/energy charge;

b) Taxes on energy use, for example;

c) Another option would be to have global permitting systems for emissions or for using a global environmental resource, allowing for trade between countries in such permits or in emissions offsets. The Montreal protocol in fact opens the door to this by allowing international exchange of CFC quota under the agreed maximum;

d) One could also think of various types of sanctions against free riding or non-compliance, as parts of international agreements, including trade sanctions (see, however, chapter 8);

e) Countries could be motivated to participate in agreements by compensation payments and by so-called "joint implementation" programmes (see below).

As in the case of national policy instruments, these instruments may aim at an incentive effect (especially a and b), or they could be intended to raise financial resources to undertake other activities including emission abatement. In fact, the revenue raising character of some of these instruments might appear as an advantage given the large amounts of financial resources likely to be needed to address adequately the global problems and the distributional aspects that would be encountered in attempts to obtain global commitments. Other sources of revenue for addressing global environmental issues might be taxes on, for example, trade or income, such as the proposal by, inter alia, Norway and the Netherlands to have a 0.1 per cent tax on GNP.

Countries are sovereign with respect to their national environmental policies and policy instruments, subject to international agreements that they have entered. Regarding global environmental issues they may join in with collective efforts to achieve certain reductions and thereby employ a range of different instruments at the national level. They may also voluntarily move ahead in fields where international agreement is not yet sought or achieved and employ, at the national level, instruments addressed at global problems. There are two aspects worth mentioning in this respect.

The first is, that mechanisms for exchange of information and coordination are important so that harmonisation is sought where desirable or so that undue divergence and distortions do not arise. PPP is an important principle in this respect and needs to be universally adopted. On-going interest in economic instruments employed with reference to global environmental issues is called for.

The second issue is that of compliance and the stability of the agreement. Agreements may differ widely in terms of the distributions of costs and benefits to the various participants over time, and the relative significance of these costs and benefits may change due to the economic developments of these countries. Mechanisms should be developed that ensure compliance and here, too, information and discussion must go on.

7.3.3   Contextual elements and instrument choice

Criteria for selecting specific (economic) instruments to deal with global environmental issues do not fundamentally differ from those pertaining to instruments' selection in general (see chapters 2 and 5). They can be summarised under:

-- (environmental) effectiveness
-- economic efficiency
-- (social and political) acceptability - Amongst the acceptability criteria distributional considerations are especially important, particularly in the context of global environmental issues (as compared with national ones or perhaps even regional ones).

Using simple models, it can be shown that a pro rata agreed emissions reduction approach is less efficient in economic terms, than applying either charges or tradable in permits to achieve the same reduction [*e.g.*, Barrett in OECD (1991d)] - but this is theory. It ignores much of the lack of data and knowledge on effectiveness and efficiency, and overlooks the acceptability problem and all that it stands for. As with the national policy instruments (and perhaps even more so), contextual issues need consideration. They may explain why approaches vis-a-vis global environmental issues may differ from one to another, why some agreements come off the ground more easily, and they may suggest different mixes of instruments to be used in different cases.

a) To begin with, there are many complexities on the environmental side. Global environmental issues have complex causes (*e.g.*, global warming, as triggered by a multitude of different gases), source strengths may be difficult to establish or monitor, and environmental processes may intervene, for better or for worse, without these processes being understood adequately at present. That is, there may be much uncertainty on causal mechanisms, dose-effect systems, sources. If that is the case, designing an economic instrument will tend to be a lengthy exercise with very intricate negotiation on its base, calculation, *modus operandi*, enforcement and monitoring.

b) There are substantial differences in the societal structuring surrounding both sources and receptors. There may be few sources (as in the case of CFC-producers) or many (as with CO_2). Sources may be concentrated in some countries or dispersed over many. On the receptor side, conditions may differ in terms of wealth, relative priority for the environment, etc. In fact, there may be a connection between the two, in so far as environmental quality is "income elastic" and/or developing countries are facing extra severe budget and income constraints in addressing their own as well as collective environmental concerns. Also, costs and benefits of abatement may be insufficiently known, and they may be unevenly distributed geographically or in terms of economic sectors. Moreover, different international economic instruments could work out differently in terms of the associated distributions of costs and benefits. The latter point might even be compounded if there were to be divergence in the way national governments translate their international environmental commitments into national policies and instruments.

c) Differences in conditions with respect to the levels and distributions of (marginal) costs and benefits of abating global environmental degradation may explain why international cooperation on these problems is or is not coming about. And this may be important for understanding where compensations are to be used.

If the benefits are low and the costs are high, cooperation might not add very much in achieving overall optima and hence might not come about. Where the benefits of abatement are high and the costs are relatively low, countries might already take individual action or easily find each other. Stimulating international cooperation might be potentially relevant when both benefits and costs are relatively low or are both relatively high, especially in the latter case where stimulating cooperation might be relevant from a collective point of view.

Economic rationales for stimulating cooperation exist where differences in (marginal) benefits and costs between countries are present. In the case of ozone depletion the immediate benefits might be high for some countries involved and low for others, whereas total benefits in the longer run are substantial. At the same time there are relatively few, and easily identifiable and monitored sources and the costs of avoiding emissions of the relevant gases are relatively low. One would expect cooperation to be potentially important in this case, and to come about relatively easily, as is indeed the case. As far as the greenhouse problem is concerned, individual costs may differ but can, on the whole, be very significant economically. At the same time, benefits are (as yet) not undisputed and unevenly distributed. If the benefits of reducing emissions of greenhouse gases were high, then cooperation would be potentially rewarding (and vice versa, hence there appears to be a rationale for the fact that international agreement on this issue appears to take much more effort to come about - Barrett in OECD (1991).

Prospective modelling work suggests that the impacts of instruments (charges and permits) on revenues and income transfers between countries can be very important [Hoeller *et al* (1992)].

In the case of (transboundary and) global environmental problems a special issue arises out of the combination of the criteria of effectiveness and efficiency. It may well be more effective to allocate a certain amount of money to financing environmental activities elsewhere. Alternatively, in order to achieve a certain environmental objective in terms of overall contributions to a specific environmental problem, it may be cost-effective to invest in activities beyond the jurisdiction of the country concerned. This may provide considerable negotiation space between countries in searching for international agreements. It is important to recognise that countries can contribute to the global abatement effort in three different ways [Jones (1992)]: i) domestic abatement at their own expense; ii) payment for abatement activities in areas beyond their jurisdiction; iii) in giving permission for abatement activities to be financed by other countries.

In paragraphs 4 and 5 below, we will first focus on two "pure" types of instruments, charges and tradeable permits, and then (in par. 6) move to mixed options as are now being reviewed and discussed in the context of real policy development processes.

7.4 Emission charges

Charges on contributors to global environmental problems would make processes and products that generate the pollutants concerned inherently less attractive. Thus, charges, if correctly calculated of course, directly add to more transparency in the market. Prices reflect full costs better than in the absence of environmental policy measures or when such measures are taken but do not show up in cost and price levels. On first sight, charges may therefore appear attractive.

Charges on emissions can, in several cases of global environmental problems (*e.g.*, CFCs, fuel related CO_2) be related to products. In such circumstances, the administrative framework for collecting the charge may be relatively easy to conceive, or may, in some cases, already function in some parts of the world. In most countries and for many fuels, systems already exist for taxing them. Furthermore, changing the level of a charge or tax is a relatively simple intervention, compared with altering other instruments (such as tradeable permits).

Emissions charges could be implemented at the national level by countries agreeing to use this instrument. There is only a need for a relatively modest institutional requirement at the supranational level.

The question does of course arise as to what the proper tax base should be. One or a few polluting substances, or the entire range? But once this choice has been made and once some estimate as to the desired overall reductions exist, the theoretical case for charges is clear, that of static and dynamic efficiency. We have already seen that, when it comes to charges at the national level, there is little quantitative evidence to support this convincingly, and there are no examples yet of an international instrument to retrospectively show empirical light on this issue. Moreover, the alternative economic instrument of tradeable permits is equally attractive on theoretical grounds. So, on second sight there does not appear to be a clear-cut, *a priori* case.

Let us turn to a more specific case, that of a carbon or carbon/energy tax. In relation to global warming, taxation may best be based on energy content or on Carbon content (or some combination of these two). Carbon taxes are now applied in the Nordic countries (including Finland) and the Netherlands, but only in the Norwegian and Swedish case are they significant enough to have an incentive impact (see chapter 4). Presently, the European Community is considering a carbon/energy tax on energy, raising primary energy prices initially by $3, going up to $10 per barrel of oil equivalent some 7 years after the scheme becomes operational.

Some economic issues to discuss in relation to the energy/carbon charge and its prospects, are the domestic distributional consequences (including fiscal aspects) and their macro economic and structural impacts. Other, more familiar [see *e.g.*, OECD (1992f)] elements in any discussion on practical tax systems are, tax base, tax rates, agents and institutions.

7.4.1 Distributional/fiscal impacts

Energy taxes are applied to a commodity with fairly low short term price elasticities. Hence, in order to achieve a given quantity impact on its consumption, the price rises must be high. In order to achieve a levelling off of CO_2 emissions in 2020 at the 1990 level, calculated emission taxes vary between $30 to $150 per ton of carbon [Barde (1992)]. This implies high tax revenues and raises the question as to the distributional impacts of such a taxation policy.

There is a case to be made for using these revenues as part of overall public finance, which, in the case of an assumed fiscal neutrality would imply that other taxes could be reduced accordingly. An additional, supportive argument might be that the revenues of a energy/carbon tax should not (all) be reinvested in energy conservation or carbon absorption activities (nor would that appear to be necessary).

In addition to the fiscal aspect, the income effects of the charge are to be considered. There may be a case for approximately neutralising such effects. At the level of income groups this is possible, as several studies show. However, full distributional neutrality is illusory. At the micro level there will always be losers and gainers.

Part of the revenue of such a tax could be used for facilitating the development of international environmental policy and its institutions. Part of it could be used to influence the direction of technology [OECD (1992e)]. Such "earmarking" of the revenues of environmental charges is an issue for further debate, as the revenue could and perhaps should primarily be used as a source of public finance, allowing for tax cuts elsewhere [OECD (1993a)]. One argument against earmarking is that if prices are correctly reflecting environmental costs in consequence of a "proper" tax level, then earmarking would lead to a distortion of the optimal allocation. On the other hand, the "recycling" of revenues into sectors raising them and using them to finance environmental investment may effectively enhance acceptance of tax instruments, and might speed up cleaning up programmes.

7.4.2 Macro-economic and structural impacts

Substantial emissions reduction efforts may induce significant feedbacks to the economic process. Work has been done to explore the economic costs of e.g., reducing carbon emissions, in various countries. OECD has recently completed its second survey of the macroeconomic costs of reducing CO_2 emissions [Hoeller et al (1992)]. From this, it is concluded that achieving large reductions of energy related CO_2 emissions may depress growth rates of world GDP by 0.2 percentage points, but this can nevertheless imply reductions in the long run levels of global GDP of some 3-8 per cent (between 2025 and 2050). Some national models (e.g., for Norway, Netherlands, Sweden) predict higher growth rate depressions with higher GDP impacts earlier on (2000-2010) at much lower levels of reduction [Hoeller et al (1992)]. These are very tentative figures but they provide some background.

Moreover, sizable charges could lead to substantial shifts in the industrial structure [Hoeller et al (1992), p.41]. In one country's exploration of the economic impacts of unilateral and joint (OECD) action via carbon/energy charges (without exemptions), national (and even some collective) sectoral implications could be dramatic for the very energy-intensive sectors [CPB (1992)] and even reflect themselves in relocation of industries with most of the regional emissions reduction resulting from that, rather than from fuel shifts, energy conservation or new (leaner) technology. The latter study abstracted from possible mitigating (trade) measures correcting for distortions between participants and non participants in the charge scheme. Of course such measures (as well as exemptions for industrial energy users competing internationally beyond the jurisdiction of the charge agreement) would affect these results.

Unless agreements could be reached with all important trading partners, countries will not easily impose extra costs on their industries through high energy or carbon taxes [OECD (1992f)]. To protect their international competitive positions, countries usually consider tax schemes only if associated with substantive exemptions for domestic energy-intensive industries operating on international markets. In the context of regionally applied charging schemes, one theoretical alternative to such exemptions could be, mitigating measures on transboundary transactions correcting for cost differentials due to non participation in the charge scheme (see chapter 8 on trade issues related to economic instruments). Providing exemptions and mitigation may easily lead to different consequences in terms of internal and external support for policies aimed at global environmental issues and little is known of these and other indirect effects of such corrective measures. The current (1993) proposal for an EC CO_2/energy tax appears to favour an approach based on exemptions.

7.4.3 Prospects

All OECD countries have energy taxes, though at different levels and using different operational systems. Some countries have or are considering effective energy/carbon charges, and others look at raising energy tax levels. It is difficult to evaluate the changes in support for, or acceptance of this instrument in the various OECD countries, as these changes do not point in one direction, yet from this point of view there may be scope for a charge or tax based approach.

The charges/tax option is an appropriate one given the wish to improve market signals and to raise public awareness. Due to the elasticities involved however, they may not be the most effective way to modify behaviour in the short run.

Macro economic impacts or the fear of such impacts, might make countries reluctant to move ahead of others in introducing such charges, or in making them high enough to have an incentive impact. On the other hand, they might introduce charges and simultaneously exempt larger energy users. The latter practice would reduce the effectiveness of charges systems. Especially in the case of charges there are very solid grounds for engaging in an international dialogue on them, explicitly taking into account impacts on international trade and investment, on relocation, etc, as resulting from a substantial tax.

A gradual approach, moving from fairly low (and hence in the short run ineffective) levels of taxation to higher level seems preferable to introducing a high tax immediately. Low levels of energy/carbon taxation can only be regarded as revenue raising devices and not as proper economic incentives.

7.5 Tradeable permits systems (TPS)

The main idea of tradeable permits is achieve an environmental target at least cost to society, by setting an emissions reduction target, distributing or auctioning permits up to the total set by the reduction target, and by allowing trade in these permits. Compared with charges, permit trading has the advantage of a more certain result in terms of emissions reductions. The amount of permits issued sees to that, if it is enforced. These permits can be subjected to market forces. There can be more of them for sale if further technological innovation results in cleaner technologies. Demand, if mobilised, will competitively force prices down to their appropriate level.

There must be an information system (containing information about potential buyers and sellers) and an agreed auction procedure. Also, there must be some agreed initial endowment and this is one of the main difficulties with a TPS. In addition, there are operational conditions to be met (see chapter 3), *e.g.*, on the definition of the market, the 'size' of the market in terms of numbers of buyers and sellers, of real possibilities for trade in terms of actual or potential cost differentials, etc.

Several of these issues will be briefly reviewed.

7.5.1 Market definition

Like in the case of charges, the commodity in which trading is to occur, has to be defined clearly. Even in the case of greenhouse forcing alone, there are several options (*e.g.*, fossil CO2 emissions, ibid plus C-sequestration by plantation, net CO_2 emission, equivalent CO_2 including other gases, etc.). The choice of definition is likely to reflect the performance to be expected on a number of criteria, such as compatibility with sustainable development, efficiency, etc (see chapter 8). There seems to be a growing consensus that limiting trade to emissions of energy-related carbon dioxide is the most feasible initial option [Swart, in OECD (1992e)], with that of including other CO_2 sources and sinks as a very promising alternative especially as it may do more justice to the claims of developing countries [Agarwal and Narain (1991)].

7.5.2 Market power

With limited numbers of market actors there is the risk of parties being capable of manipulating permit prices, or to influence prices in related commodity markets (Tietenberg) in order to affect the distribution of rents. According to Roland (1992), this risk is relatively low [see also Bohm (1991)]. Yet, there is another distributional issue related to market power. With unequal purchasing power and in a buyers' market, the possession of permits might be concentrated in the portfolios of a few rich nations.

One solution to the problem of market power confusing the performance of trading schemes would be to limit the period during which rights of emission remain valid. Under such circumstances hoarding and accumulating emission rights would be much less economically rewarding. Taking this to an extreme would almost turn TPS into a complicated charging system. There is a balance to be sought here, since reducing the life span of a permit will make trading less interesting.

7.5.3 Initial endowments

The question of how to distribute initial rights is a crucial one in obtaining international support for any large scale trading system. This initial endowment or distribution could be based on current emissions level, past responsibility, equality of effort, GDP, population, etc. Grubb and Sebenius [in OECD (1992f)] suggest that the initial allocation will have to be a compromise, based for example on both a per capita allocation and current emission levels.

7.5.4　Tradeable permits and sink enhancement

If countries also engage in activities that enhance their environments' capacities to absorb or buffer global pollutants, then they could be compensated for that within a trading system if such activities would yield additional permits or credits to them that could subsequently be offered on the permits market. There are, however difficulties associated with this option, *e.g.*, establishing the contribution to sink "size".

7.5.5　Other issues

Several other major difficulties have been identified [see for example, OECD (1993b)], such as:

-- determining an appropriate balance between comprehensiveness of coverage (in terms of substances as well as sources) and the cost of monitoring;

-- applying the system to emissions as produced by the informal or traditional sectors of especially developing economies;

-- designing effective and efficient international controlling institutions.

7.5.6　Prospects

Important advantages of a system of tradeable emissions permits include:

-- an efficient way of achieving predetermined objectives in terms of emissions;
-- greater flexibility in comparison with location-bound standards.

Yet, various institutional and distributional aspects of a permits system render it difficult to get accepted. At the global level there are as yet no institutions to appropriately and adequately handle the complexities (both politically and technically) of trading in emission rights between countries. Much of the empirical evidence on trading schemes suggests, that "making the jump ....to the far more complex problem of greenhouse gases ... may ultimately prove to be too unwieldy for existing political institutions to accommodate (especially over the short term)" [Jones and Corfee-Morlot, OECD (1992e)]. The latter authors and Grubb and Sebenius (op.cit.) have identified design criteria for tradeable permit systems.

7.6 Avenues for further policy development

7.6.1　Introduction

Economic instruments do have a part to play in tackling global environmental issues. The wider the geographical extent within which they are applied, the larger are the efficiency and flexibility benefits of applying these instruments likely to be. However, it is also fair to observe that both economic instruments considered above (*i.e.*, taxes and tradeable permits) to deal with global environmental problems, meet with a number of problems including:

a) Difficulties in establishing their base - the emissions of which compounds should be charged, and permits on what, should form the tradeable commodity? Going for the ideal situation in terms of contribution to the problem at hand, might lead to rapidly rising costs of implementation, assessment, monitoring, etc. This might preclude a timely conclusion of global agreements to deal with these problems;

b) Such new instruments are to be implemented in situations where other environmental policy instruments (*e.g.*, national policies) and earlier, bilateral agreements may already be in operation, or in situations that are also affected or even governed by other policies (*e.g.*, GATT). Care must be taken to ensure that market and government failures (see chapter 2) will not be compounded by this, but rather that such failures are tackled and reduced (at least in the long run).

c) Absence of universal support.

7.6.2   *Economic instruments and sink enhancement*

Countries, apart from being sources of substances or other interventions giving rise to global environmental problems, may also engage in activities that enlarge the environment's capacity to absorb (or otherwise handle) human activities. In the case of climate change, sink enhancement *e.g.*, through agricultural and reafforestation policies is a case in point. Economic instruments may support such activities. In the case of charges, if only net emissions are charged, or emissions corrected for the annual impact in terms of sink enhancement, then the latter would be economically attractive and so would, of course, innovation. A similar argument holds for allowing trade in credits built up by sink enhancement or technological innovation.

However, the issue of the measurement of the contribution to resolving global environmental problems through sink-enhancement is such an intricate one, that it might preclude advancement in international environmental agreements, unless put aside until better monitoring is possible. In terms of environmental "content" the most practicable way forward may be a phased one starting with emissions only, and incorporating sink enhancement later. This is yet another aspect where a pragmatic approach requires first steps based on a reduced scope.

7.6.3   *Charges and TPS's compared*

So far in this section, we have discussed (de)merits of economic instruments in general. We now proceed by comparing the two main categories of instruments.

Advantages of TPS over a charges system include [Bohm (1991)]:

-- the relative certainty of meeting emissions standards;
-- complications with revenues in non-convertible currencies;
-- difficulties in relation to domestic policies having indirect effects on domestic fossil fuel use;
-- the relationship between the global tax and existing domestic energy taxes.

Some relative advantages of a tax system over TPS are [Bohm (1992)]:

-- the revenue raising nature of the instrument;
-- the familiarity of governments and other actors with the excise tax principle;
-- low transaction costs.

In addition, Bohm mentions as an advantage of the tax system that it would not give rise to a compromising dominant position of large industrial countries. However, against this, one may put the fact that a tax-cum-transfers system might, in their perception, put developing countries in a situation of structural dependency on industrial countries, as opposed to the situation under a tradeable quota regime, in which their position would be based on agreed upon rights.

We add to this listing of relative merits of charges, that appropriate international institutional frameworks to operate a charges system is relatively easy to conceive.

With respect to a charge, the uncertainty about their environmental effectiveness poses an important problem. This could partly be resolved by resorting to an iterative or trial-and-error approach starting with low levels that are manipulated upwards over time, but this poses another type of uncertainty to economic agents, with important dynamic implications affecting acceptability.

Both systems, that of tradeable permits and of charges, suffer from difficulties in obtaining wide support. In the case of tradeable permits, compensatory side payments, an "equitable" initial endowment and temporary exemption of poorer countries could be necessary to (gradually) introduce a worldwide system. In the case of taxes the revenue raised by it could be (partially) recycled on the basis of income effects of the tax, initial income differentials, efforts in developing or installing cleaner technology or augmenting pollution sinks, etc, so as to enhance international support. Yet, trading schemes appear to, at best, offer a future option only. Practical difficulties provide impediments to their rapid introduction. Charges or other schemes including stepwise approaches and hybrids of the two types of instruments discussed here, may be more attractive in the short run. Some attention will be given now, to such approaches.

7.6.4   *Towards new approaches*

At several points in this chapter, attention was drawn to the fact that "sub-optimal", partial and mixed approaches may be necessary to multilaterally address global environmental issues and to select instruments for such collective efforts, if progress is to be made. Examples of such in-between approaches already are being discussed or tried out. Some of these will be given here.

We start by pointing out some options for partial, sub-global introduction of agreements and instruments for addressing global environmental issues. When considering such partial schemes, it is important to note that both the environmental effectiveness and the economic efficiency would most likely be lower compared with global or more comprehensive applications of TPS or charges.

a) For a number of reasons [OECD (1992e)], it appears that a system of national taxes on energy or carbon could be achieved easiest at the regional level. This might hold particularly in the European region (some details on an EC carbon/energy charge were given above). Subsequent introduction of similar charges elsewhere could lead to harmonisation towards for example, an OECD-wide charge. The larger the geographical scope of the charge, the less need there is to exempt industrial sources on the basis of distortions in long term comparative cost differentials and competitive positions, or to use other complicating additional measures.

b)   Also, a system of trading in emissions permits or offsets would presumably, only start with a group of developed economies (such as OECD) participating, on the basis of internationally agreed (national) emission targets. Such countries could be allowed to buy reductions elsewhere (offsets).It is important to design procedures that could facilitate the gradual development of a true market for entitlements out of bilateral transfers of such entitlements in the initial phases [Roland (1992)].

c)   The "tradeable warming credits" of Yang and Rosenfeld [in OECD (1992e)] provide another example of embarking on a road that could ultimately result in a proper market to arise. Offset trading as a first step may be attractive to developing countries that would not be bound yet by agreed targets so that there would be no direct constraints on their economic development.

d)   Another intermediary step towards a full permit trading situation, may be that of "joint implementation". Under a regime of joint implementation, countries might find it in their interest to participate in an agreement and to take on emissions reductions responsibilities, whilst the financial consequences would be shared with or adopted by other participants. From Western Europe, acid deposition offsets are being sought and financed in Central and Eastern Europe as an alternative to carry out costly abatement programmes in for example, the Netherlands (1993).

e)   A practicable "second best" approach with either charges or TP-systems might be to accept a less than across-the-board-approach and to focus on certain main contributors/sources to global problems, building up from there towards a more complete system.

It is important that possibilities for such partial participation schemes be identified and evaluated. For obvious reasons, the question of how to relate to non-participating countries will be a very important one, in such cases. Non-participation should not be rewarded with substantial economic benefits to be reaped on the markets of participating countries, at least not on a permanent basis, and this may lead to a search for sanctions in for example the trade area. Examples include, import tariffs compensating for cost level rises induced by participation, and rebates when exporting to non-participating countries (see chapter 8).

Incentives should be designed to encourage participation. Side-payments, exemptions and temporary reimbursements might be elements to consider in seeking to enhance participation. Special attention should also be given to the conditions under which such schemes are appropriate. In a way they can be regarded as justified by the fact that often the countries providing these compensations are those that now and in the past have been largely responsible for the present state of the environment. In that sense it is still the polluters (or one category of them) paying (to other polluters). It is in fact one category of polluters enabling another to engage in environmental policies when its income constraint is an over severe impediment.

Other instruments are of a mixed or hybrid nature, or could develop in that direction.

i)   Funds drawn from the revenue of national charges for *e.g.*, energy use and/or carbon emission, could be set up to finance environmental expenditure in developing countries;

ii)   Tradable credits could be built up by abating emissions in other countries, based *e.g.*, on unit rates to be decided in international agreements;

iii) Due to differences in contextual or institutional backgrounds (see chapter 2) no specific system might meet with ready support elsewhere. In such situations, mixed systems might arise with charges in some regions and emissions permit trading elsewhere;

iv) a system has been suggested with two distinct but fairly low levels of taxes (one on carbon or energy consumption up to a certain level, the other, higher rate to be paid beyond that level) to feed into an international fund, and with trading options between countries [Yang and Rosenfeld, OECD (1992f)].

The partial and hybrid systems discussed here, may have institutional advantages in that they often build on well known procedures such as negotiations in terms of reduction efforts, or in that they may be developed in the context of an already operational framework such as, that of the Climate Convention and the international negotiations on climate change. Such schemes, while avoiding some of the problems posed by straightforward trading schemes, may however lead to other difficulties:

i) In as far as co-operation of developing countries is required, these might show reluctance in going along with programmes that apparently imply financial transfers with "new conditionalities" (the proviso that they be spent on specific activities targeted to deal with specific reductions in emissions) involved.

ii) In cases of joint implementation or emission fund schemes, difficulties in establishing the environmental effectiveness are likely, as this involves difficult assessments of time paths of emissions with and without the programmes, against the background of often relatively unpredictable developments at the level of the underlying economic activity levels.

iii) Moreover, some of these schemes entail the exchange of property rights on natural resources in other countries. It could be difficult to disentangle environmental effectiveness from considerations in terms of expected capital gains.

7.6.5   *A tentative assessment*

International environmental negotiations are increasingly initiated to tackle global environmental issues. Principles for international environmental policy are needed and the OECD-Polluter Pays Principle is foremost amongst these. Other principles have been established (Declaration of Rio) and new practices are emerging.

Economic approaches to global issues are important to build into the emerging conventions and institutions aspects such as flexibility and efficiency. This also holds for the instruments to be used. As in cases of sub-global environmental problems, several types of instrument may be considered. Recently most attention has been given to systems of charges and tradeable permit systems.

Looking at the economic efficiency (and disregarding a number of institutional and political impediments), fully fledged schemes of emissions charges or tradeable emission permits appear most (and equally) attractive. If their effectiveness were to be the criterion, tradeable permits hold the promise of more certainty in comparison with charges.

But considering the acceptability of the various instruments, there are difficulties with the equity aspects (both initial endowments and issues related to accumulation) and the institutionalisation rendering tradeable permit schemes politically ill-acceptable, compared with charges or taxes on energy.

In terms of environmental effectiveness a step-by-step approach starting with some system applied by a small number of countries, gradually increasing its geographical scale and incorporating more elements of charging and/or trading, with a gradual level of price rise in the case of a charge, appears to be the most promising and practicable avenue for an international climate change policy.

On-going discussions about a carbon/energy charge in Europe, perhaps later on to be introduced OECD wide as a second step to a global scheme, are very important in this respect.

"Joint implementation" of emissions reduction where some countries participate financially and technically in other countries' abatement or sink enhancement efforts, is another one.

References

AGARWAL A. and S. NARAIN (1991), *Global Warming in an Unequal World: a Case of Environmental Colonialism*, Centre for Science and Environment, New Delhi.

BOHM, P. (1991), *Policy Problems of International Cooperation on the Global Environment*, Paper presented at the International Conference, "Economy and Environment in the "90s", Neuchatel, Aug 1991.

CPB (Central Planning Bureau) 1992.

HOEL M. (1991), "Global environmental problems: the effects of unilateral actions taken by one country". *Journal of Environmental Economics and Management*, Vol. 20, No. 1, pp 55-71.

HOELLER P., A. DEAN and M. HAYAFUJI (1992), "New Issues, New Results: the OECD's Second Survey of the Macroeconomic Costs of Reducing CO2 Emissions". Working Papers, No. 123. OECD Economics Department, OECD, Paris.

JONES T. (1992), "Cost effectiveness and Implementing the Climate Change Convention", *International Journal of Global Energy Issues*, Vol 4, Geneva.

MÄLER K.-G. (1990). "International Environmental Problems", *Oxford Review of Economic Policy*, Vol 6 No. 1, Spring.

OECD (1976), *The Economics of Transboundary Pollution*. OECD, Paris.

OECD (1989), *Economic Instruments for Environmental Protection*, OECD, Paris.

OECD (1991), *Environmental Policy: How to Apply Economic Instruments*, OECD, Paris

OECD (1991d), *Responding to Climate Change: Selected Economic Issues*, OECD, Paris.

OECD (1992e), *Climate Change: Designing A Tradeable Permit System*, OECD, Paris.

OECD (1992f), *Climate Change: Designing A Practical Tax System*, OECD, Paris.

OECD (1992g), *International Economic Instruments and Climate Change*, OECD, Paris.

OECD (1993a), *Taxation and Environment: Complementary Policies*, OECD, Paris.

OECD (1993b), *Convention on Climate Change: Economic Aspects of Negotiation*, OECD, Paris.

ROLAND R. (1992), "From Offsets to Tradeable Entitlements", UNCTAD Study on Tradable Carbon Emissions Entitlements, DRAFT. ECON Energy Oslo 1992.

UN (1992), "Rio Declaration on Environment and Development", UNCED, A/CONF.151 /PC/W G.III/L.33/Rev. 1.

Chapter 8

Overview of The Trade Effects of Economic Instruments(4)

8.1 Introduction

This chapter will discuss the general advantages and disadvantages of economic instruments versus regulatory instruments from the perspective of international trade; the means by which economic instruments can have both price and non-price effects on trade; the differential effects of various types of economic instruments, including user charges, taxes, tradeable permits and deposit-refund systems; the use of economic instruments and current trade rules; and the use of economic instruments in international environmental agreements. This discussion is mostly directed to the use of economic instruments for pollution abatement rather than for resource conservation, about which less is known. It is intended as a preliminary overview of the potential trade effects of economic instruments. The OECD is carrying out further research and analysis in this area.

8.2 Trade advantages and disadvantages of economic instruments

Using economic instruments to implement environmental policies may have certain advantages and disadvantages relative to regulatory instruments from the standpoint of the trading system. Most of this discussion is conjectural, since: i) economic instruments, although increasing in use in the OECD countries, still play a limited role in the overall implementation of environmental policies; ii) economic instruments have generally not been used in isolation but as "add-ons" to regulatory instruments; and iii) economic instruments have not been used frequently in a way to have a significant effect on the behaviour of producers.

Greater use of economic instruments in implementing environmental policies is being advocated because theoretically the use of economic instruments can have three main advantages depending on the design and implementation of the instruments and the situation. These potential advantages, all of which have implications for international trade, are: 1) the efficiency gains sometimes associated with economic instruments; 2) their greater transparency; and 3) their lesser potential for manipulation by non-governmental interests.

First, economic instruments, if properly designed, can have advantages in terms of the efficiency with which they achieve environmental objectives relative to regulatory instruments. Such efficiency gains could imply reduced negative effects on the international competitiveness of domestic producers. Regulatory instruments have certain static inefficiencies in ignoring the pollution abatement cost differentials of firms. They also have certain dynamic inefficiencies in their relative weakness in

---

4.   This chapter has been written by the OECD Secretariat.

promoting technological change and innovation. In certain situations, economic instruments can be more flexible in taking into account the marginal abatement costs of different producers, in allowing producers to trade on the comparative advantages reflected in their different abatement costs (in the case of tradeable permits), and in encouraging firms to identify and develop technologies with lower abatement costs. The efficiency characteristics of economic instruments can possibly lower the overall costs of environmental protection and minimise adverse effects on the competitiveness of domestic firms.

Second, economic instruments (particularly product taxes) are generally thought to be more transparent than regulatory instruments in the implementation of environmental policy and thus allow for easier understanding and adaptation by trading partners. In the development of regulatory instruments, domestic firms will have advantages with regard to advance information on technical specifications for products which are to be met within a certain time period. Foreign competitors may suffer a time-lag disadvantage and also technical difficulties in adapting their products to the new regulations. In contrast, product taxes are relatively straight-forward in their application to domestic and imported products and do not generally give advantages to particular groups or firms. In addition, when product taxes are applied to imports, the imports will still be allowed market entry while foreign producers make adaptations to reduce the rate of the environmental tax. In the case of both regulatory and economic instruments which are predicted to have a significant impact on trade, transparency can be increased through complying with the notification and consultation procedures under the General Agreement on Tariffs and Trade (GATT).

Third, it is proposed that, in some cases, economic instruments may be less vulnerable than regulatory instruments to manipulation and influence by established interests and thus less liable to serve protectionist purposes. Domestic firms usually play a role in the development of environmental policies, which naturally reflect the environmental concerns and capabilities peculiar to the implementing country. These firms can, through negotiations, influence the product specifications mandated by the regulation, the technologies to be used, and the compliance period. The design of regulatory instruments, particularly product standards, can be used to shelter domestic firms from foreign competition or give them certain trade advantages. Economic instruments, particularly environmental taxes and charges, are thought to be more straightforward in their design and less capable of being manipulated to serve domestic interests, either directly or indirectly.

However, these theoretical advantages of using economic instruments have not been tested widely by experience and may not hold true for all types of economic instruments. It is difficult to generalise as to whether economic instruments have advantages for trade over regulatory instruments which will depend on the particular situation where they are applied (and such factors as market structure, demand and supply elasticities, etc.). In general, economic instruments are not inherently "less trade-distortive" than regulatory instruments; the trade effects of economic instruments will also depend on the instrument in question and its design.

· For example, environmental taxes and charges have often not been set at a high enough level to have effects on the relative competitiveness of domestic producers. Although they may be more efficient in achieving certain environmental goals than regulatory instruments, high levels of environmental taxes will likely raise costs and prices and disadvantage domestic firms in international trade. It is possible that environmental taxes which are expected to have significant competitive impacts (*e.g.*, carbon taxes) may be subject to manipulation and influence by domestic groups. Similarly, greater transparency may be a characteristic of environmental product taxes, but tradeable permit systems and deposit-refund schemes can be opaque to foreign producers and entail the same adaptation problems as regulatory instruments. These instruments can also unintentionally disadvantage imports and favour domestic producers, although this does not necessarily imply a trade distortion.

8.3 Types of trade effects

In general, economic instruments (like regulatory instruments) can have two types of effects on international trade, namely price effects and non-price effects (Table 8.1). Price effects are incurred when the use of economic instruments affects the costs of producers which may be passed on in the prices of their products and influences the price-competitiveness of these products in international trade. Price effects are more likely in the case of user charges and environmental taxes; the relative price effects will depend on the level or rate of the charge or tax and its design, particularly whether certain sectors are exempted or subject to lower rates of tax.

Non-price effects are incurred when the use of economic instruments affects the market access afforded to imported products or to foreign producers. Non-price effects are more likely in the case of tradeable permit systems and deposit-refund schemes, particularly when the design of these systems makes it more difficult for foreign firms to invest or to sell their products in domestic markets. However, this does not mean that tradeable permit systems and deposit-refund schemes do not have price effects or that taxes and charges may not affect market access. Table 8.1 simply indicates the main types of trade questions which have been associated with the different types of economic instruments.

Table 8.1 **Primary trade effects of economic instruments**

Intrument	Price effects	Non-price effects
User Charges	xx	
Environmental Taxes	xx	
Tradeable Permit Systems		xx
Deposit-Refund Systems		xx

8.4 Types of economic instruments

8.4.1 *User charges*

User charges differ from other types of environmental charges and taxes in that they are generally intended to raise revenues rather than to stimulate more far-reaching changes in the behaviour of firms. User charges thus normally have a revenue-raising rather than an incentive function. User charges are also generally associated with a return flow of goods and services whereas some other environmental charges and taxes are not. Thus, revenues from user charges are most often used to pay for measures that will further reduce the emission of pollutants, while revenues from environmental taxes might more often be allocated to the general government budget. In practice, these distinctions are sometimes difficult to make and the terms user charges, environmental charges and environmental taxes are often used interchangeably. In the case of most user charges, firms pay a fee for a service rendered such as waste removal or the treatment of effluents.

User charges, as defined here, are often levied at low levels. Although they raise costs for firms and can have price effects, user charges should not have significant impacts on the competitiveness of firms. In addition, the incidence and level of user charges are relatively similar among the major trading partners. In general, user charges with a revenue-raising objective constitute such a small increment to operational costs that they unlikely to have severe price or competitiveness effects.

8.4.2   *Environmental taxes*

Environmental taxes, as defined here, differ from user charges in that they are usually intended to alter the behaviour of producers and consumers (much like regulatory instruments) and are not generally payments for environmental services. Environmental taxes can be levied on both products and processes with the intent of shifting production or consumption away from some product or practice towards a more environmentally-friendly product or practice. This, however, will depend on the rate or level at which the tax is set. Environmental taxes calculated to be genuine incentives to change behaviour can lead to substantial cost differentials, price effects and competitiveness effects.

Both *Product taxes and emission taxes* can increase costs for producers, often because they are levied on top of regulatory requirements for product or process changes. The increased costs and corresponding price increases can affect the competitiveness of domestic producers in domestic and foreign markets relative to producers not subject to such taxes. To date, however, most environmental taxes have had limited incentive effects in altering environment-related behaviour. They have had only small price effects because these taxes have not been translated into substantially higher product prices, and they have had minor impacts on international competitiveness. This is because most environmental taxes are still in an early phase of implementation, have not been established at high rates, and/or are adjuncts to regulations.

Although environmental taxes are more often associated with price effects than with non-price effects, they could have implications for market access. Product taxes set at differential rates based on product characteristics or components might create a potential for market segmentation. Foreign suppliers could face increased difficulties in adjusting product qualities to different markets in seeking lower tax rates. In addition, Product taxes, such as on different types of packaging materials, can implicitly discriminate against imports when applied at higher rates to materials or components used predominantly for imported products. Emission taxes set at high levels can create disincentives to foreign investment.

Carbon taxes - A special type of product tax

Much of the analysis and debate about the trade effects of economic instruments have surrounded proposals for the introduction of carbon taxes, designed to address the problem of climate change, (see chapter 7). Carbon taxes are usually applied as environmental product taxes on the carbon content of fuels, in order to limit emissions of carbon dioxide - one of the "greenhouse gases" that are suspected of promoting global warming. Analyses of existing and prospective carbon taxes, as well as national and international emission modelling exercises, indicate that *effective* carbon taxes (*i.e.*, ones that are high enough to induce significant changes in emissions of carbon dioxide) are likely to cause noticeable effects on competitive relationships and trading patterns, through changes in trade in products and investment shifts (see chapter 7).

Generally imposed on top of existing taxes on fossil fuels, carbon taxes have already been levied in Denmark, Finland, Norway, Sweden, and The Netherlands. The possibility of implementing such taxes is also under active study in Switzerland and the European Community. Although all carbon taxes imposed to date have been introduced for the purpose of limiting emissions, they are all relatively new, making it difficult to find strong evidence yet of significant changes in emission behaviour at either the production or consumption levels of these economies. All carbon taxes that have been implemented to date have been designed to reduce emissions, rather than merely to raise revenues for the taxing authority. This behavioural objective is underlined by the fact that these taxes have also been introduced in conjunction with reductions in other existing taxes, usually energy taxes, apparently in an effort to maintain some form of "revenue neutrality" overall.

As with any policy instrument, the competitive effects of carbon taxes will tend to differ at the macro-economic level, being generally more severe in smaller countries where the trade intensity is higher, where the energy-intensity of the economy is greater, where the available options for circumventing the effects of the tax are greater (via tax exemptions, for example), and where the market power of the country in the global economy is lower. At the micro-economic level, the trade effects will generally depend on the energy-intensity of individual industries. On this basis, the industries most likely to be affected *a priori* by a carbon tax are iron and steel, petrochemicals, non-ferrous metals, and non-metallic minerals. Exemptions or lower taxes for some sectors may imply higher taxes on other sectors, with implications for production and trade patterns. Both the short-term and long-term effects of carbon taxes on the competitiveness of domestic firms will ultimately depend on the level of the carbon tax and the design of sector exemptions and rebates. It will also depend on whether the country is a net importer or net exporter of energy, because carbon taxes may affect net importers differently from net exporters.

Because of the potential disruptions in trading patterns that could result from imposing carbon taxes unilaterally, all countries that have introduced these taxes so far have offered some form of exemption to their most energy-intensive industries (tax reductions, subsidies, etc), using the plausible argument that simply displacing the economic activity from a taxed country to an untaxed one would do nothing to reduce global emissions. At the international level, this "leakage" issue has dominated much of the policy debate about climate change, although the experts seem divided on the amount of "leakage" that might actually occur as a result of unilateral abatement action. One way of reducing this problem would be to introduce a carbon tax only if a country's major trading partners also agreed to introduce similar or equivalent measures. This is, in fact, the idea that has underpinned much of the debate about a carbon-energy tax in the European Community.

The competitive effects of carbon taxes will depend on the substitution response of the country (macro level) or the industry (micro level) to tax-induced changes in relative prices. Relative price changes should cause one of three basic things to occur: demand for carbon-intensive products may fall; energy efficiency may increase; or technological developments may be induced. "Time" is an important variable in all three of these possibilities. For example, it is generally suspected that the response of the economic system to a given level of carbon tax will increase over time, implying that the long run trade effects will be less than the short run effects. On the other hand, if a country/firm has already increased its energy efficiency (or made substantial investments in new technologies) in the past, it will be less capable of "squeezing" new economies out of the system today, and therefore, less able to use "time" to minimise the impact of the carbon tax on competition.

In considering the desirability of changes in competitiveness resulting from the imposition of carbon taxes, it is important to consider two key points. First, a carbon tax is only imposed because of a failure of the market place to force producers and consumers of carbon-intensive fuels to take the full costs of their activities into account in their economic decisions. In economic terms, therefore, carbon dioxide emissions are an "externality" produced by the production and consumption of carbon-intensive products. Eliminating *part* of this externality would probably improve total economic welfare. To the extent that the carbon tax reflects this goal, we may conclude that some shifts in consumer/producer behaviour (and therefore in trade patterns and competitiveness) would actually *improve* global economic conditions.

Second, the size of the required carbon tax simply reflects the value that society places on the externality. In other words, the greater the cost of doing nothing about the problem of global warming, the larger the required carbon tax will be. Note, however, that this is true of *any* policy instrument. The higher the expected social cost, the more intensive the policy response should be, and the larger the disruptions in existing trading patterns *should* be.

8.4.3   *Tradeable permit systems*

Tradeable permit systems begin by setting emission reduction targets for specific pollutants, or for specific geographic areas. They then distribute permits to the level of these targets, using some method of allocating the initial permits. Recipients of these permits are then free to trade them in the marketplace. There are several problems associated with actually applying tradeable permit systems in practice, as well as several advantages from using such an approach, where this is feasible. In this sense, tradeable permits are no different from any other policy tool that may be chosen to redress an environmental problem.

Similarly, tradeable permit systems designed to limit greenhouse gas emissions will generate most of the same types of trade effects that carbon taxes or regulatory regimes will. Firms or countries which need to emit greenhouse gas emissions will face higher costs than they did before the system was implemented. This will lead to shifts in comparative advantages, and therefore, to shifts in trading patterns and competitiveness.

Although there is limited experience with tradeable permit systems, these can potentially function in a way to deter investment, either domestic or foreign. Designing operable tradeable permit systems is difficult. Problems may be encountered in terms of too few buyers and sellers, miscalculations regarding the number of permits, and strategic behaviour on the part of participants. New entrants may find it difficult to buy into such systems when the permit markets are not functioning well. In addition, certain firms may receive an advantage when initial quotas are "grandfathered" or given to established companies, who may also participate in the design of the tradeable permits system. More stringent pollution control requirements may be imposed on new firms or installations increasing their marginal abatement costs. A number of factors in the design and operation of tradeable permits systems can potentially discriminate against new investors (including domestic and foreign investors) who wish to invest in the area and participate in the tradeable permits system.

8.4.4   *Deposit-Refund schemes*

The trade impacts of deposit-refund schemes lie not so much with the financial incentive measures of the system, *i.e.*, the deposit charge and subsequent refund, but rather with the additional requirements and costs of participating in the scheme. Deposit-refund schemes are not new and have been in existence for decades. It is only recently with greater international trade in beverages that the trade implications of such schemes have been called into question. Most deposit-refund schemes in the OECD countries are intended to promote the recycling and re-use of beverage containers but tend to be extended to a number of packaging materials and products (see chapters 3 and 4).

Deposit-refund schemes can potentially act as non-tariff barriers to trade and give competitive advantages to domestic products, either intentional or unintentional. In general, whether domestic or foreign, firms with a limited market share and firms distant from the market may face disadvantages in participating in deposit-refund schemes. Foreign suppliers may be placed at a comparative disadvantage relative to domestic suppliers who can more easily create or purchase facilities or services for storing, recycling and/or reusing the containers in question. The costs of market entry will be higher for foreign suppliers if they have to invest in the physical infrastructure of a collection and re-use system for their products in foreign markets or if they have to transport containers back to home markets for reuse or recycling. Domestic suppliers may cooperate in setting up collection, recycling, and/or re-use facilities and benefit from standardisation and economies of scale as well as the proximity of the market. They may also participate in the design of the system, which can act to discriminate against foreign suppliers depending on the types of containers and the market share of the containers included in the deposit-refund scheme.

8.5   Economic instruments and trade rules

The use of economic instruments in environmental policy should be compatible with international trade rules as given in the General Agreement on Tariffs and Trade (GATT) to avoid undue trade distortions and also disguised protection of domestic producers. In general, the use of economic instruments should be in accordance with the principles of national treatment (*i.e.*, they should be applied to domestic and foreign products in the same manner) and non-discrimination (*i.e.*, they should apply equally to imported products from all sources). Care must also be taken in designing environmental policies based on economic instruments that these do not unintentionally create severe disadvantages for foreign suppliers in terms of market entry and foreign investment.

In order to allow countries to levy taxes without greatly disadvantaging the competitiveness of domestic producers, GATT includes rules for "border tax adjustments" which provide for certain taxes to be levied on imported products and rebated for exported products. According to these provisions, the tax rate on domestic and foreign products should be equivalent and taxes should not be imposed on foreign products where similar domestic products are exempted. Furthermore, as elaborated in the GATT panel report concerning a dispute involving the U.S. Superfund Act, border tax adjustments are allowed in cases of environmental product taxes and taxes on inputs to the product. The use of import levies and export rebates to adjust for environmental process taxes, such as emissions and effluent taxes, is discouraged. These rules are based on the principle of the "country of destination" whereby products are taxed in the countries where they are consumed to avoid double taxation. Conversely, environmental process taxes should only be levied in the "country of origin" and not adjusted at the border. There have been questions raised regarding the ability to levy border taxes in conjunction with carbon taxes. These address, specifically, whether the energy or fuel used to produce a good can be considered an input to the product and therefore an environmental tax on this fuel can be adjusted at the border on similar imported products.

8.6 International environmental agreements

There is increasing attention being given to the potential use of economic instruments, such as environmental taxes and tradeable permit systems, to implement international environmental agreements. Existing international environmental agreements, including the Basel Convention on Transboundary Movements of Hazardous Wastes, the Convention on International Trade in Endangered Species (CITES) and the Montreal Protocol on Substances that Deplete the Ozone Layer, have relied mainly on quantitative restrictions to achieve their environmental objectives. Under the Montreal Protocol, however, several countries have used economic instruments to achieve the phase-out of the use of ozone-depleting substances at the national level. Emerging international environmental agreements on climate change, preservation of biodiversity and management of tropical timber resources could possibly make greater use of economic instruments, both environmental taxes and tradeable permits, in their regulatory regimes.

Economic instruments in an international environmental context are theoretically attractive for the following reasons. First, in certain situations, they can facilitate more efficient and less costly approaches to addressing global and transboundary environmental problems. Evidence suggests that there are large differences in the marginal costs of pollution control between countries, largely related to differences in economic development. International agreements can build on economic instruments which take these cost differentials into account and allow countries to profit from comparative advantages in pollution abatement costs. Second, the use of economic instruments in the framework of an international environmental agreement may, in some cases, promote fuller internalisation of environmental costs and a more equitable sharing of the burden of addressing environmental problems, thereby limiting distortions to international trade. Third, the revenue-raising characteristics of certain types of economic instruments can facilitate funding obligations and the transfer of financial resources to less developed participants in an international environmental agreement.

Some economic instruments (such as high levels of carbon taxes) may only be used in the context of an international environmental agreement, rather than by individual countries, due to the need for the simultaneous introduction of such measures by major trading partners to avoid undue competitive effects on domestic producers (c.f. the "conditionality clause" of the EC carbon-energy tax proposal). Countries will be reluctant to introduce high levels of carbon taxes and apply them to energy-intensive sectors unless similar taxes are implemented by their major foreign competitors. Countries also may introduce carbon taxes in conjunction with a variety of "offset policies", such as exemptions, subsidies and border tax adjustments in order to mitigate negative effects on competitiveness. Governments will need to cooperate in further clarifying rules for such offset policies in the environmental field to avoid trade distortions and disputes.

In the absence of an international environmental agreement, greater harmonization of the use of economic instruments at the national level, like increased harmonization of environmental policies generally, would be valuable from the trade perspectives. In order to achieve transboundary and global ecological objectives, governments could more fully coordinate their domestic use of environmental taxes and tradeable permit systems to make them more efficient and effective in addressing similar environmental problems. In order to minimise disruptions to the trading system and avoid constituting barriers to trade, governments could cooperate in the design and implementation of environmental policies based on economic instruments and ensure their transparency and equality of access to foreign suppliers. In general, governments could more fully harmonize the use and implementation of economic instruments by coordinating the timing of the introduction of economic instruments, the broad level and design of the schemes, and the industrial scope of their application.

References

BAUMOL, W.J. and W.E. OATES (1988), *The Theory of Environmental Policy*, Cambridge/New York, Cambridge University Press.

BOERO, G., R. CLARKE, and L.A. WINTERS (1991), *The Macroeconomic Consequences of Controlling Greenhouse Gases: A Survey*, London, University of Birmingham.

BUCHANAN, J.M. and G. TULLOCK (1975), "Polluters' Profits and Political Response: Direct Controls Versus Taxes", *American Economic Review*, Vol. 65/1.

CROPPER, M.L., and W.E. OATES (1992), "Environmental Economics: A Survey", *Journal of Economic Literature*, Vol. XXX.

EUROPEAN COMMISSION (1992), "A Community Strategy to Limit Carbon Dioxide Emissions and to Improve Efficiency, Brussels", EC.

HUFBAUER, G. (1993), "The Evolution of Border Tax Adjustments", Washington, D.C., Center for Strategic Tax Reform.

OECD (1993), *Environmental Policies and Industrial Competitiveness*, Paris, OECD.

PEZZEY, J. (1991), "Impact of Greenhouse Gas Control Strategies on UK Competitiveness", London, University of Bristol.

VERBRUGGEN, H. (1991), "Contours of a Sustainable International Trade System", *Internationale Spectator*, Vol.45, No.11.

UNCTAD (1992), "Combating Global Warming: Study on a System of Tradeable Carbon Emission Entitlements".

PART IV

CONCLUSIONS AND PROSPECTS

Chapter 9

Economic Instruments for Environmental Policy: Conclusions, Discussion and Prospects

9.1 The starting point: The use of economic instruments in 1987

Environmental policy has made use of economic instruments for a long time. User charges in relation to water pollution and glass bottle deposit refund systems testify to this. But how widespread was this, and how representative of environmental policy interventions?

In OECD (1989) a review was presented of the situation in the OECD Member Countries in 1987. A similar survey was carried out to assess the 1992/3 situation. The second survey excluded certain types of instruments such as subsidies, liability, administrative charges.

Basing ourselves on the 1993 enumeration of economic instruments, the 1987 survey revealed that a total of at least 100 economic instruments, or some 7 per country surveyed, were in operation. However, a closer look disclosed that many of these instruments were of little significance and most of them were not really intended to have an incentive impact. Less than half had the intention of generating an economic incentive and only one third may have effectively had some incentive impact.

Basically then, in 1987, environmental policies in the OECD Member countries were command-and-control policies with some financial and economic add-ons.

Economists have always pointed out at the inefficiencies of standards approaches in cases where the marginal costs of environmental improvement and pollution abatement would differ, and they have often drawn attention to the allocative distortions arising from prices that do not reflect full environmental costs. They tended to see advantages of using economic instruments in terms of environmental effectiveness and economic efficiency. These include, cost-effectiveness and associated welfare gains, flexibility, and incentives for environmentally friendlier decisions on product and process innovations.

The expectations on how the use of economic instruments might develop from 1987 onward, can be summarised as follows. In the 1987 survey, three main policy tendencies, potentially influencing the role of economic instruments, were identified: a) a reduction of government intervention (deregulation); b) increased policy integration; and c) a shift of attention from curative to preventive policies. These developments were expected to result in a stronger role for economic instruments, notably (product) charges and deposit-refund systems, to harmonisation of the use of instruments, to harmonisation of economic instruments applied in different sectors, and to design of new, broad-based economic instruments.

9.2 Questions on the use of economic instruments

Some questions arising from the above are:

    a) to what extent has this picture changed since 1987?
    b) to what extent have 1987 expectations materialised, and
    c) should they be modified in the light of the experience since 1987?

Before dealing with these questions some new developments since 1987 are identified (par. 9.3). After discussing these changes, factual developments in the use of economic instruments are looked at (par. 9.4).

Further questions arising out of recent developments in environmental problem recognition and policy, have to do with extending the use of economic instruments to unexpected (in 1987) fields and implications of an extended use:

    d) can one extrapolate from OECD to the situation of economies in transition?
    e) what expectations exist on the practicability of economic instruments for dealing with global environmental issues?
    f) what prospects and impediments do economic instruments offer for/in international trade?

These are the subject matter of paragraph 9.5.

Paragraph 9.6 will draw on recent experience and the previous paragraphs to deal with questions b and c.

9.3 What has changed since 1987?

The most striking development since 1987 has been the growth in the interest in the subject of economic approaches and instruments, theoretically, empirically and in terms of policy interest.

9.3.1 Changes in policy context

On changes in policy interest, a long list of incidences could be presented, though this is restricted to some of the more important ones below:

    a) The Brundtland-UNCED process with its rising concern over how to merge environment and economics in decision making. PPP has become an increasingly well established principle likely to gain even more ground in future. It is explicitly referred to in the Declaration of Rio (the non-binding set of principles for international environmental policy that emerged from UNCED). UNCED Declaration of Rio Principle 16 reads, "National authorities should endeavour to promote the internalisation of environmental costs and the use of economic instruments, taking into account the approach that the polluter should, in principle, bear the cost of pollution....". This is almost a global recognition for some of the things that OECD has stood for in the area of environmental policy development since 1972 PPP and, later, the use of economic instruments.

Furthermore, PPP is developing in various directions. Its scope has sharpened, it is extended to broader ranges of environmental policy, such as, "user pays", "extended PPP", etc. Principles for international environmental policy are needed such as PPP, but other principles are being established (Declaration of Rio) and new practices are emerging.

b) The increased tendency to rely on market based approaches, not only in OECD countries but also in economies in transition and many developing countries.

c) Also, environmental policy attention has shifted. Environmental policy since the end of the 1980's has become more interested in tackling environmental problems at higher spatial levels such as continental and even global problems. At that level there certainly is much less scope for a command-and-control approach and hence economic instruments become more interesting options.

Environmental policy has also become more interested in diffuse and mobile sources. Again types of sources for which some economic instruments (especially product charges and deposit-refund systems) provide effective approaches.

d) The debate on environmental policy instruments is drawing global interest and appears to be embarking on new avenues in order to accommodate the demands of international environmental policies in a world of differences in terms of levels of development and access to resources. If it took 20 years to convince the world of the importance of PPP, it will also take time for the use of economic instruments to develop and spread.

9.3.2   New elements in diagnosis

In current discussions on economic instruments some new elements have emerged or some specific aspects now receive much more attention than in 1987. These include:

a) The explicit reference to institutional failure as a background to environmental externalities.

Environmental degradation has its roots in the economic process (notably, its relation to types and levels of economic activities, and their development), but also in the way decision making on economic activities and policies has been institutionalised. Conditions pertaining to the institutions that direct the economic process from within (i.e., the government and "market failure") are such that government interventions are needed to ensure the incorporation of environmental externalities.

This is far from saying that government intervention is a sufficient condition for resolving the environmental issues confronting us today:

-- governments may fail to intervene in the right places or with appropriate instruments,

-- they may inadequately address existing policy and administrative failures either because of inappropriate analysis or diagnosis, or because they are not equipped to effectively correct market processes.

b)   The recognition of the diversity of application contexts and the relevance of this for instruments selection.

The effects of policy instruments depend on the economic, political and administrative context in which they are applied. The complexities of the interactions between environmental and economic processes, as well as the dynamics of innovation preclude straightforward and simple broad-brush recommendations on which instruments to use.

c)   Awareness of the risk of failure accumulation.

Existing regulations and policy interventions may create a setting in which efficiency-based consideration of environmental policy instruments would at best indicate second-best solutions. Internalising externalities via economic instruments may not make much sense in a world of seriously distorted markets (*i.e.*, in a complex situation involving multiple market and government failures). In fact, the overall result may be ambiguous.

The need to remove old institutional failures (*e.g.*, hidden or explicit subsidies and distortionary taxes) is now more broadly recognised.

d)   Growing interest in harmonisation.

There is a need for at least considering harmonisation of countries' instrumental approaches when international trade and investment patterns are likely to be affected.

e)   An increasingly pragmatic approach.

Partly based on empirical studies (see 9.3.3), there is much less dogmatism or rhetorics in the dialogue on environmental policy instruments. A pragmatic approach is beginning to prevail, in which one no longer is categorically in favour of, or against certain types of instruments, and in which the interest is in realistic assessments of the pros and cons of different mixes of instruments in the specific policy contexts and application contexts within which they are to operate.

f)   Financial needs, especially in developing countries and European Economies in transition.

There is a, perhaps, growing need for funds for financing environmental measures. This need may support the use of economic instruments, especially charges, which may have incentive side effects.

9.3.3   *Improved knowledge and better assessment*

The present state-of-the-art can be summarised in the following points:

a)   "Rational" policy makers would select instruments so as to achieve their objectives in an optimal manner (that is, with reference to criteria such as effectiveness and efficiency) and with reference to the "concordance" of instruments with current political trends or policies (*e.g.*, compatibility with principles such as "the polluter pays"), societal acceptability, compliance/enforcement aspects, etc. Whether this assumed rationality of the process of instruments selection is indeed appropriate, is a matter for empirical research, but environmental economics can contribute by feeding that process with information on the basis of their analyses of the short and long term effectiveness and efficiency, indirect effects (on *e.g.*, trade and investment, trade-offs with other policy objectives, and institutional appropriateness.

b) (Semi-) quantitative performance criteria to evaluate (in an ex-ante setting) environmental policy instruments are now standard research practice. They cover effects or impacts on: i) environmental quality; ii) sectoral and national levels of production or productivity and employment; iii) income, consumption, purchasing power or welfare; iv) investment and relocation; v) administrative costs and revenue flows; vi) effects on income distribution, sectoral income shares, etc.; vii) cost levels, profitability and competitiveness; viii) international trade and balance of trade impacts.

Qualitative performance criteria used, include: i) acceptability; ii) legality; iii) compatibility/concordance with policy principles.

c) Surprising as this may be, there is far too little empirical evidence to arrive at a systematic ex-post evaluation of the significance of instruments as used in practice (see notably chapter 4). Much of the recommendations arrived at in this report actually originate from incidental observations and sometimes even observation driven intuitions. Further work to develop evaluation methodologies and collect evidence is needed (see also section 9.6).

d) Nevertheless, the potential policy relevance of economic instruments for environmental policy no longer rests on theoretical or academic arguments only. The call for increasingly stringent environmental quality standards in the short run inevitably means rising policy-response costs and therefore enhances the appeal of cost-effective market-based instruments. Economic instruments are also potentially relevant in policy contexts that are based on a preventative approach.

e) Economic incentives appear to operate best in combination with, or in support of, other instruments such as direct regulation. Economic incentives alone will not effectively and/or efficiently deal with environmental problems, whether national or international ones. Arguments for this include, a reinforcing dynamic incentive over and above static regulations, and the stimulus on arriving at agreements if the alternative is a stringent system of economic instruments.

f) The impact of charges and other economic incentives on the rate and direction of innovation is a much claimed advantage of such instruments but actual outcomes are not yet sufficiently well documented. There is a risk on the side of the regulator, however, that more interventionist policy may stimulate the 'wrong' technological trajectory.

g) Although the empirical work still is in its early days, progress is made in the development of tools to gauge impacts and indirect consequences of new policy instruments. There is a need to extend this work especially in the direction of integrated chain approaches and in incorporating other structural elements of the context of application (see par. 2.3.2). There also is a need to improve the decision analytical framework to assess the merits of alternative instruments (see 5.2.3).

h) With respect to the context of application, characteristics related to sources of pollution and related to the impacts of it, must be distinguished. In many cases, a general analysis of these features provides indications as to the appropriateness of the various categories of instruments.

i) Context-specific and often complex (*i.e.*, mixes of elements of command and control, incentive and suasive natures) instruments will still have to be developed and improved. New approaches emerging as potential instruments are:

-- input charges;
-- substance-based deposit refund systems;
-- agreements-*cum* enforcement incentives as alternatives to charges;
-- voluntary charging systems as now proposed within some branches of industry in *e.g.*, Germany.

9.4 The use of economic instruments since 1987

This OECD Project on economic instruments has surveyed the actual and potential use by OECD member countries, of a number of environmental policy instruments, namely, emissions charges (including user charges), product charges, deposit refund systems, tradeable permits and enforcement incentives. Conclusions based on the reported situation are summarised below. After doing that, some important caveats with respect to deriving quantitative judgements are presented.

9.4.1   *Changes since 1987*

a) Since 1987, the use of economic instruments appears to have intensified. Comparing 1987 data with "solid" 1992 indications (chapter 4), the number of economic instruments in the 8 countries we know most about (see table 4.11), has grown by some 25 per cent. Including also the instruments put in operation since 1992, the growth in the number of economic instruments used in those countries is closer to 50 per cent.

Looking at the totals for all OECD countries that we have information on for 1987 and 1993, the growth in reported use of economic instruments would be even larger, but this might be due to the 1992 survey being more accurate.

b) Instruments that have particularly been introduced more frequently, are product charges and deposit-refund systems. In the 8 countries of which we know most and comparing 1992 with 1987, the increase in these instruments amounted to 35 per cent and 100 per cent respectively. This tendency appears to have gone on after 1992.

c) Emissions charges are not really used more frequently in 1992, as far as we can tell, in the 8 countries we know best. If we look at instruments introduced after 1992, then there may have been a small increase in the reported number. If we look at all OECD countries of which we have information both on 1987 and the present, then there appears to have been an increase, but again, this may also reflect a more complete survey of instruments in 1993.

d) User charges for waste collection and disposal and for sewerage and sewage treatment are quite common in OECD countries.

e) The general practice with respect to allocating emissions charges' revenues still appears to be to earmark them for environmental expenditure. Even with regard to charges with a stated incentive purpose, the revenue raising aspects of these charges still prevail.

f) Tax differentiations in the automobile transport sector are applied widely in OECD countries. In most cases market shares of unleaded petrol have risen substantially after the introduction of a tax differential.

g) Deposit refund systems still function mainly in the field of beverage packaging and could be used much more frequently.

h) On incentive impacts or the significance of the instruments, too little information exists to provide firm judgements.

Looking at the available information (*i.e.*, basing ourselves on solid data on the 1992 instruments), we find that on emissions charges one can say with some confidence that an incentive impact now is intended in some 45 per cent of the charges (whereas in some 30 per cent it is not), but in about 90 per cent of the cases the information on actual incentive impacts is inconclusive or unavailable.

With respect to product charges we know that incentive impacts were intended as much as they were not (45 per cent in each case). When it comes to actual incentive impacts, there is inconclusive (or no) data on close to half the applications and such effects seem to be absent in at least close to 40 per cent. That information may be inconclusive has to do with the fact that very often product charges are applied in conjunction with other instruments.

The USA Emissions Trading Programme has achieved cost savings but the number of trades has remained lower than expected; more incentive impacts might be expected from the Acid Rain Control Allowance Programme. The Lead Trading scheme has performed quite well.

Evaluations of the impact of real incentives charges are highly recommendable.

i) Looking at individual countries and discounting for non-federal instruments, the Nordic countries appear to be leading in the application of economic instruments, especially product charges. Judging from data on other countries in the vanguard of environmental policy development, this does not at all imply that having ambitious environmental programmes is identical with using economic instruments with a high frequency.

Compared with the 1987 situation in the 8 best known countries, changes have been extensive in Finland, Sweden, USA, moderate in the Netherlands and minor in France, Germany and Italy.

j) Charges' revenue rebatement, or recycling revenues via environmental funds may enhance the acceptability of charging schemes.

k) It has proven to be impossible to derive systematic, quantitative information as to the fiscal or economic significance of especially charges.

9.4.2   Qualifications to these conclusions

In interpreting the above conclusions, attention must be paid to a number of points having to do with the solidness of the information provided and its generally qualitative nature:

a)   Counting instruments is obviously risky, as instruments differ in their quantitative and qualitative significance. Nevertheless, as a very rough, first approximation it is acceptable;

b)   Not every increase in the number of economic instruments is an improvement *per se*. In some cases the use of other instruments might have been preferable from an environmental economics perspective, with either another economic instrument, or another type of instrument being used altogether;

c)   The figures on incentive impacts are at yet no more than a first approximation;

d)   One source of change in the significance or incentive impact of economic instruments would be, differences in rates and tariffs applied since 1987. However, these are not documented satisfactorily.

e)   The present survey does not deal with all economic instruments. Instruments such as administrative charges, subsidies and liability have been excluded.

9.5   New domains for economic instruments?

9.5.1   Economies in transition

Economies in transition are faced with the double task of improving the efficiency of their economies and of dealing with the environmental performance of the production system which they inherited.

The question arises whether and to what degree economic instruments for environmental policies should now be put in place, and whether the experience in OECD countries provides useful insights in that respect.

The following issues figure prominently in the current debate about taxation and environment in the economies in transition:

a)   The effectiveness of incentive charges in the transition phase - It is conceivable that charges, even if the rates are high, will be passed on through product prices without any impact on the polluter's environmental performance. Also, hyper inflation may erode the incentive impact of real, unindexed, charge rates;

b)   Scarcity of administrative resources - This phenomenon practically rules out the imposition of complex schemes. At the same time one can derive from this scarcity an argument in favour of introducing instruments in already functioning administrative contexts, such as taxation agencies;

c)   Economic and political impacts of incentive charges - The fear of significant adverse economic consequences from speeding up environmental policy in economies in transition might pose an important impediment. Here the experience of OECD countries in terms of what the economic impact has been on for example, the sectoral cost levels of the introduction of environmental policies might provide comforting second thoughts. Also, OECD countries' experience suggests the positive impact on acceptability of, advance announcement, stepwise rates rises, consultation with economic sectors, temporarily subsidising pollution control, rebating charges' revenues, exempting pollution-intensive industries;

d) Financing environmental expenditures - Economies in transition typically operate "environmental funds" to finance their environmental activities. OECD experience suggests that earmarking might be acceptable as a transitional measure but that in the long run this needs to be readdressed;

e) The timing of environmental taxes - Now, or after the transition period? The overall impression is that environmental measures including charges, etc, should be part of the on going restructuring of the economies in transition rather than being postponed to form a second, painful round of restructuring in the future;

f) Most economies in transition at least on paper have charges on pollution and payments for natural resource use rights. Charges typically are too low to be effective and resource use payments still often imply substantial elements of hidden subsidies to the users;

9.5.2 *Global environmental problems*

Although regulations have tended to be the "instrument of choice" in addressing *domestic* environmental problems, economic instruments probably have a role to play in tackling *global* environmental issues, mainly because of their potential contribution to improved economic efficiency. With pollution problems increasingly being viewed in international terms, more attention is being paid to the economic efficiency of emission abatement programmes. The ozone, global climate change and acid rain debates have each contributed to this process. A greater focus on the economic efficiency objective tends to increase the likelihood that economic instruments will be used more in the future.

But efficiency is only one important objective of environmental policy. If economic instruments are to be successfully applied to international environmental problems, they will also have to deliver at least some environmental improvements and be perceived as being equitable in their distributive impacts. Since no policy instrument can usually deliver on all of these objectives at the same time, economic instruments will typically be used in conjunction with other policies, such as regulations.

Another point to keep in mind is that countries have very little experience with international economic instruments. Most of the practical experience with tradeable permits comes from the United States, but none of this experience involves international applications. Similarly, no international environmental tax yet exists, and the recent EU proposal for a carbon/energy tax has yet to be approved. Some experience does exist, however, with the international harmonisation of taxes other than environmental taxes, especially in the European Union. Applying this experience to the environmental field could increase the potential use of international economic instruments considerably.

Many of the pros and cons of applying taxes or tradeable permit systems at the international level were discussed in Chapter 7. It is clear from these discussions that the general application of these instruments at the global level remains some way off. At the very least, the large degree of cultural and institutional heterogeneity that exists at the international level will make it difficult to reach agreement on economic instruments across broad groups of countries. The more homogeneous the base to which an economic instrument is applied, the easier it will be to obtain international agreement on the fairness (equity) of the international burden-sharing arrangement, but the fewer economic efficiency gains will be available from using economic instruments in the first place. Conversely, a high degree of international heterogeneity suggests that large economic savings may be available from cooperation, but that it may be difficult to reach an acceptable burden-sharing arrangement. This phenomenon is already being observed in the climate change debate, where the negotiations are not yet converging on a policy response that involves economic instruments, despite the large efficiency gains that seem to be available from using them.

On the other hand, opportunities for more limited applications of economic instruments may exist at the sub-global, but still international, level. The economic efficiency gains to be derived from more limited systems would also be limited, but could still represent improvements to what would otherwise have been possible. Examples of such approaches might include:

a) a system of national taxes harmonised at the regional level. The proposed EEC carbon-energy tax is one example of this, but it may also be feasible to think of other types of regional aggregations for harmonised taxes/charges (such as the OECD Group);

b) regionally-accepted tradeable permit systems for dealing with only certain types of international environmental problems (*e.g.*, acid rain);

c) mixed systems, involving some attributes of taxes, tradeable permits, subsidies, and regulations.

One example might be "joint implementation", where countries invest in emission abatement activities internationally, in order to take advantage of cost-savings available elsewhere. Joint implementation is really a "loose" form of tradeable permit system, where the resource transfers from one country to another could eventually be financed by the "earmarking" of funds raised in domestic (but internationally harmonised) carbon taxes.

Overall, both tradeable permits and taxes may be practical for use in responding to some types of international environmental problems, perhaps even eventually at the global scale. For this reason, a case can be made for "starting small" and building up to a global system incrementally. This would allow the practical experiences gained on a regional basis to eventually be brought together into a coherent framework at the global level.

9.5.3 *Economic instruments and trade*

Economic instruments, like regulatory instruments, can have impacts on international trade in terms of both price effects and non-price effects. These effects, however, will depend on the instrument in question and its design. User charges, or those environmental levies aimed primarily at raising revenues for a service rendered, and environmental taxes may have price effects in raising costs for producers which are passed on in the prices of products and influence the price-competitiveness of these products in international trade. Non-price effects may be more likely in the case of tradeable permit and deposit-refund schemes, particularly when the design of these systems makes it more difficult for foreign firms to invest or to sell their products in domestic markets.

However, economic instruments are expected to have certain advantages over regulatory instruments, depending on the situation. If properly designed, economic instruments can have efficiency advantages in taking into account the marginal abatement costs of different producers and in encouraging firms to develop new technologies. They might then have reduced negative effects on competitiveness. Economic instruments may be more transparent than regulatory instruments and thus allow for easier understanding and adaptation by trading partners. In addition, in certain cases, economic instruments may be less vulnerable to manipulation and influence by established interests and less liable to serve protectionist purposes.

In order to levy taxes without greatly disadvantaging the competitiveness of domestic producers, countries might consider the use of border tax adjustments. Trade rules allow for import levies and export rebates in conjunction with environmental product taxes, but generally not to adjust for environmental process taxes. Greater use of economic instruments might be considered for the implementation of international environmental agreements. More harmonization of the use of economic instruments at the national level could be helpful in moderating adverse trade impacts. This might include coordinating the timing of the introduction of economic instruments, the broad level and design of the schemes, and the industrial scope of their application.

9.6   Outlook

Certainly, in many OECD countries, the level of intensity of environmental policy has developed since 1987. Since the previous report on the use (in 1987) of economic instruments in OECD Member Countries [OECD (1989)] the use of these instruments has indeed grown. Moreover, the domain in which they are applied, has expanded and still is doing so. In part this can be explained by a growing policy support of economic instruments which now appears to be becoming world-wide.

There are substantial differences in the rates at which economic instruments are applied. And different sets of these instruments appear to be tried out in different parts of the world. One can still observe a wide range of opinions as to when and where to apply which type of instrument or mix of instruments.

The relative roles of economic instruments and direct regulation might be changing, and they even might alter in favour of economic instruments, but this is certainly not a very clearly observable tendency yet, since also the use of other types of instruments may have evolved since 1987.

Nowhere is there an observable change towards replacing the basic command-and-control approach by a purely economic one. Economic instruments are complements mostly and substitutes only sometimes for other types of approaches.

It is to be expected, that new principles, for example, based on solidarity, past accountability, cost effectiveness or future collective interest, will have to be developed to complement the polluter or user pays principle. The "victim pays" option and conditions under which it might be made operational as a principle, are to be elaborated. The overall context is likely to be, the (extended) Polluter and User Pays approach.

Options for integrating environmental considerations in other sectors' policies are far from having been exhausted. In fact, OECD countries are now witnessing the beginning of such integration efforts. Economic instruments and generally instruments that bring market signals closer to their socially desirable levels, have important roles to play and this has increasingly become common insight. Environmental taxation may be one specific area in which this policy integration can take place, but the relationships to the fiscal framework as such, must be further worked out [(see OECD (1993)].

The exact extent to which damage costs are, or should be included in PPP, has yet to be established.

Economic instruments are now increasingly being considered for application at the regional/global level. Global or regional energy charges or carbon charges are being discussed, global and tradable carbon quota are being investigated, etc. OECD rightly plays a leading role here and should continue to do so.

9.6.1   New developments and expectations

Some important new developments, the impact of which are as yet difficult to assess, are:

In eight countries so far, official task forces are carrying out feasibility studies on the use of economic instruments and/or ecotaxes. Another six countries have formally announced that they intend to use economic instruments increasingly;

On-going discussions about a carbon/energy charge in Europe, perhaps to be later introduced OECD wide as a second step to a global scheme. The present US Administration's inclination to apply an energy tax may be a further step towards this;

"Joint implementation" of emissions reduction where some countries participate financially and technically in other countries' abatement or sink enhancement efforts, may become another new approach to international environmental policy;

The idea of product charges appears to be spreading. As an example, in Belgium a set of product charges is to be implemented as per 1-1-94, on beverage packaging, pesticides, paper, disposable razors and cameras.

New options for an economic approach that are emerging include:

-- less "overt" systems, such as liability, dual systems, voluntary agreements-cum-noncompliance fees or even voluntary taxes, etc;
-- fiscally neutral charges;
-- charges-cum-revenue recycling;
-- input taxes;
-- privately created and managed funds.

Possible future developments are:

a)   As environmental regulations on collective treatment of polluted water and waste are getting stricter, there is an increasing scope for user charges with incentive effects. For instance, municipalities are experimenting increasingly with waste user charges that are related to volume;

b)   The future of economic incentives depends critically on finding acceptable solutions for distributional impacts [see Harrison (1994)). Practicable formulas for rebating charges' revenues and grandfathering tradeable permits, can contribute to political and social acceptability of incentives charges and tradeable permits. The US experience with tradeable permits is of relevance here. So far, all programmes have relied on grandfathering. As for

188

charges, the Swedish NOx charge with revenues rebated integrally to polluters on the basis of their output, is important;

c) If no high quality data base is established on actual incentive effects, the often heard arguments of "ineffectiveness" or "low elasticity" will continue to be heard and constitute obstacles to a rational application of economic incentives. The same holds for the issue of administrative implementability: there is no a priori case that economic incentives are more difficult to implement but this could be supported by much more empirical evidence.

Possible impediments to introducing economic incentives include:

-- dynamic impacts and costs of change resulting from environmental policies and new instruments;
-- doubts about the real behavioural impact of economic instruments, often only visible in the longer term;
-- implicit coalitions between industry and bureaucrats and environmentalists in preferring (for very different reasons) direct regulation to the application of economic instruments such as charges;
-- the current economic recession in which any measure leading to additional costs (and a fortiori charges that go beyond making firms pay for measures only) will meet with opposition;
-- incoherence of government policies in general and even within environmental policy alone. This includes the underlying issue of conflicts between departments in terms of interests, principles, strategies;
-- governments' image in terms of reliability, when objectives and approaches of environmental policy are frequently changing (*e.g.*, trial-and-error adaptations of charge levels are violently opposed);
-- tax fatigue;
-- distributional and competitive strength-impacts.

9.6.2   What's next? Further research areas

The above underlines the need for on-going work on experiences with economic instruments (old and new) and other instruments. It also underlines the need for the identification and analysis of *impediments* to using economic instruments.

Aspects now recognised as being important in connection with instruments selection, are *not only* typical economic aspects such as the number of agents or parties involved and the slopes of marginal cost and benefit curves, but also features having to do with properties of the pollutants involved and their different fates in ecologically different circumstances. Also, the administrative political arenas in which these instruments are to be used, with their immense differences in bureaucratic cultures, relative powers of the groups involved, political systems, traditions, etc, are important. Distributional aspects will remain crucial arguments in the debates on policy instruments, especially in relation to economic instruments as in relation to these instruments the distributional aspects are so conspicuous. This implies the desirability of developing a decision-analytic framework for instrument evaluation, taking into account various features of the context of application of these instruments, and element of the policy arena surrounding this application context, both at the general and more detailed level (see chapter 5 and Harrison (*op cit*)]. Methodologies to assess the effectiveness and efficiency of economic instruments should be developed.

Some further areas of possible interest by OECD are:

-- a refined and broadened information-base on economic instruments. It is very unlikely that the surveys held so far, capture fully the use of economic instruments, their financial and incentive features. Such systematic data gathering implies the need for clear and consistent and generally accepted definitions (*e.g.*, tax-charge);

-- The areas of resource pricing and economic instruments could be looked at conjunctively and simultaneously;

-- A study of the factual dynamic efficiency impacts of economic instruments on technological innovation and on behaviour in general, with a focus on the many smaller charges, etc;

-- Further dissemination of information and experiences to emerging market economies and to developing economies, building on UNCED results (*i.e.*, acceptance of PPP and economic instruments);

-- Maintain high quality work in area of global environmental policies especially in designing new, practical hybrids, etc.

References

OECD (1993a), "A checklist of Environmental Instruments for Assessing their Potential Trade Impact", OECD Working Party of the Trade Committee, 12-14 February.

OECD (1993b), *Environmental Policies and Industrial Competitiveness*, OECD, Paris.

OECD (1993c), *Taxation and Environment: Complementary Policies*, OECD, Paris.

HARRISON D. (1994), *The Distributive Implications of Economic Instruments for Environmental Policy*, OECD, Paris.

MAIN SALES OUTLETS OF OECD PUBLICATIONS
PRINCIPAUX POINTS DE VENTE DES PUBLICATIONS DE L'OCDE

ARGENTINA – ARGENTINE
Carlos Hirsch S.R.L.
Galería Güemes, Florida 165, 4° Piso
1333 Buenos Aires   Tel. (1) 331.1787 y 331.2391
Telefax: (1) 331.1787

AUSTRALIA – AUSTRALIE
D.A. Information Services
648 Whitehorse Road, P.O.B 163
Mitcham, Victoria 3132   Tel. (03) 873.4411
Telefax: (03) 873.5679

AUSTRIA – AUTRICHE
Gerold & Co.
Graben 31
Wien I   Tel. (0222) 533.50.14

BELGIUM – BELGIQUE
Jean De Lannoy
Avenue du Roi 202
B-1060 Bruxelles   Tel. (02) 538.51.69/538.08.41
Telefax: (02) 538.08.41

CANADA
Renouf Publishing Company Ltd.
1294 Algoma Road
Ottawa, ON K1B 3W8   Tel. (613) 741.4333
Telefax: (613) 741.5439
Stores:
61 Sparks Street
Ottawa, ON K1P 5R1   Tel. (613) 238.8985
211 Yonge Street
Toronto, ON M5B 1M4   Tel. (416) 363.3171
Telefax: (416)363.59.63

Les Éditions La Liberté Inc.
3020 Chemin Sainte-Foy
Sainte-Foy, PQ G1X 3V6   Tel. (418) 658.3763
Telefax: (418) 658.3763

Federal Publications Inc.
165 University Avenue, Suite 701
Toronto, ON M5H 3B8   Tel. (416) 860.1611
Telefax: (416) 860.1608

Les Publications Fédérales
1185 Université
Montréal, QC H3B 3A7   Tel. (514) 954.1633
Telefax : (514) 954.1635

CHINA – CHINE
China National Publications Import
Export Corporation (CNPIEC)
16 Gongti E. Road, Chaoyang District
P.O. Box 88 or 50
Beijing 100704 PR   Tel. (01) 506.6688
Telefax: (01) 506.3101

DENMARK – DANEMARK
Munksgaard Book and Subscription Service
35, Nørre Søgade, P.O. Box 2148
DK-1016 København K   Tel. (33) 12.85.70
Telefax: (33) 12.93.87

FINLAND – FINLANDE
Akateeminen Kirjakauppa
Keskuskatu 1, P.O. Box 128
00100 Helsinki
Subscription Services/Agence d'abonnements :
P.O. Box 23
00371 Helsinki   Tel. (358 0) 12141
Telefax: (358 0) 121.4450

FRANCE
OECD/OCDE
Mail Orders/Commandes par correspondance:
2, rue André-Pascal
75775 Paris Cedex 16   Tel. (33-1) 45.24.82.00
Telefax: (33-1) 49.10.42.76
Telex: 640048 OCDE

OECD Bookshop/Librairie de l'OCDE :
33, rue Octave-Feuillet
75016 Paris   Tel. (33-1) 45.24.81.67
(33-1) 45.24.81.81

Documentation Française
29, quai Voltaire
75007 Paris   Tel. 40.15.70.00

Gibert Jeune (Droit-Économie)
6, place Saint-Michel
75006 Paris   Tel. 43.25.91.19

Librairie du Commerce International
10, avenue d'Iéna
75016 Paris   Tel. 40.73.34.60

Librairie Dunod
Université Paris-Dauphine
Place du Maréchal de Lattre de Tassigny
75016 Paris   Tel. (1) 44.05.40.13

Librairie Lavoisier
11, rue Lavoisier
75008 Paris   Tel. 42.65.39.95

Librairie L.G.D.J. - Montchrestien
20, rue Soufflot
75005 Paris   Tel. 46.33.89.85

Librairie des Sciences Politiques
30, rue Saint-Guillaume
75007 Paris   Tel. 45.48.36.02

P.U.F.
49, boulevard Saint-Michel
75005 Paris   Tel. 43.25.83.40

Librairie de l'Université
12a, rue Nazareth
13100 Aix-en-Provence   Tel. (16) 42.26.18.08

Documentation Française
165, rue Garibaldi
69003 Lyon   Tel. (16) 78.63.32.23

Librairie Decitre
29, place Bellecour
69002 Lyon   Tel. (16) 72.40.54.54

GERMANY – ALLEMAGNE
OECD Publications and Information Centre
August-Bebel-Allee 6
D-53175 Bonn 2   Tel. (0228) 959.120
Telefax: (0228) 959.12.17

GREECE – GRÈCE
Librairie Kauffmann
Mavrokordatou 9
106 78 Athens   Tel. (01) 32.55.321
Telefax: (01) 36.33.967

HONG-KONG
Swindon Book Co. Ltd.
13–15 Lock Road
Kowloon, Hong Kong   Tel. 366.80.31
Telefax: 739.49.75

HUNGARY – HONGRIE
Euro Info Service
POB 1271
1464 Budapest   Tel. (1) 111.62.16
Telefax : (1) 111.60.61

ICELAND – ISLANDE
Mál Mog Menning
Laugavegi 18, Pósthólf 392
121 Reykjavik   Tel. 162.35.23

INDIA – INDE
Oxford Book and Stationery Co.
Scindia House
New Delhi 110001   Tel.(11) 331.5896/5308
Telefax: (11) 332.5993
17 Park Street
Calcutta 700016   Tel. 240832

INDONESIA – INDONÉSIE
Pdii-Lipi
P.O. Box 269/JKSMG/88
Jakarta 12790   Tel. 583467
Telex: 62 875

IRELAND – IRLANDE
TDC Publishers – Library Suppliers
12 North Frederick Street
Dublin 1   Tel. (01) 874.48.35
Telefax: (01) 874.84.16

ISRAEL
Electronic Publications only
Publications électroniques seulement
Praedicta
5 Shatna Street
P.O. Box 34030
Jerusalem 91340   Tel. (2) 52.84.90/1/2
Telefax: (2) 52.84.93

ITALY – ITALIE
Libreria Commissionaria Sansoni
Via Duca di Calabria 1/1
50125 Firenze   Tel. (055) 64.54.15
Telefax: (055) 64.12.57
Via Bartolini 29
20155 Milano   Tel. (02) 36.50.83

Editrice e Libreria Herder
Piazza Montecitorio 120
00186 Roma   Tel. 679.46.28
Telefax: 678.47.51

Libreria Hoepli
Via Hoepli 5
20121 Milano   Tel. (02) 86.54.46
Telefax: (02) 805.28.86

Libreria Scientifica
Dott. Lucio de Biasio 'Aeiou'
Via Coronelli, 6
20146 Milano   Tel. (02) 48.95.45.52
Telefax: (02) 48.95.45.48

JAPAN – JAPON
OECD Publications and Information Centre
Landic Akasaka Building
2-3-4 Akasaka, Minato-ku
Tokyo 107   Tel. (81.3) 3586.2016
Telefax: (81.3) 3584.7929

KOREA – CORÉE
Kyobo Book Centre Co. Ltd.
P.O. Box 1658, Kwang Hwa Moon
Seoul   Tel. 730.78.91
Telefax: 735.00.30

MALAYSIA – MALAISIE
Co-operative Bookshop Ltd.
University of Malaya
P.O. Box 1127, Jalan Pantai Baru
59700 Kuala Lumpur
Malaysia   Tel. 756.5000/756.5425
Telefax: 757.3661

MEXICO – MEXIQUE
Revistas y Periodicos Internacionales S.A. de C.V.
Florencia 57 - 1004
Mexico, D.F. 06600   Tel. 207.81.00
Telefax : 208.39.79

NETHERLANDS – PAYS-BAS
SDU Uitgeverij Plantijnstraat
Externe Fondsen
Postbus 20014
2500 EA's-Gravenhage   Tel. (070) 37.89.880
Voor bestellingen: Telefax: (070) 34.75.778

NEW ZEALAND
NOUVELLE-ZÉLANDE
Legislation Services
P.O. Box 12418
Thorndon, Wellington   Tel. (04) 496.5652
                          Telefax: (04) 496.5698

NORWAY – NORVÈGE
Narvesen Info Center – NIC
Bertrand Narvesens vei 2
P.O. Box 6125 Etterstad
0602 Oslo 6   Tel. (022) 57.33.00
                          Telefax: (022) 68.19.01

PAKISTAN
Mirza Book Agency
65 Shahrah Quaid-E-Azam
Lahore 54000   Tel. (42) 353.601
                         Telefax: (42) 231.730

PHILIPPINE – PHILIPPINES
International Book Center
5th Floor, Filipinas Life Bldg.
Ayala Avenue
Metro Manila   Tel. 81.96.76
                         Telex 23312 RHP PH

PORTUGAL
Livraria Portugal
Rua do Carmo 70-74
Apart. 2681
1200 Lisboa   Tel.: (01) 347.49.82/5
                         Telefax: (01) 347.02.64

SINGAPORE – SINGAPOUR
Gower Asia Pacific Pte Ltd.
Golden Wheel Building
41, Kallang Pudding Road, No. 04-03
Singapore 1334   Tel. 741.5166
                         Telefax: 742.9356

SPAIN – ESPAGNE
Mundi-Prensa Libros S.A.
Castelló 37, Apartado 1223
Madrid 28001   Tel. (91) 431.33.99
                         Telefax: (91) 575.39.98

Libreria Internacional AEDOS
Consejo de Ciento 391
08009 – Barcelona   Tel. (93) 488.30.09
                         Telefax: (93) 487.76.59
Llibreria de la Generalitat
Palau Moja
Rambla dels Estudis, 118
08002 – Barcelona
          (Subscripcions) Tel. (93) 318.80.12
          (Publicacions) Tel. (93) 302.67.23
                         Telefax: (93) 412.18.54

SRI LANKA
Centre for Policy Research
c/o Colombo Agencies Ltd.
No. 300-304, Galle Road
Colombo 3   Tel. (1) 574240, 573551-2
                         Telefax: (1) 575394, 510711

SWEDEN – SUÈDE
Fritzes Information Center
Box 16356
Regeringsgatan 12
106 47 Stockholm   Tel. (08) 690.90.90
                         Telefax: (08) 20.50.21

Subscription Agency/Agence d'abonnements :
Wennergren-Williams Info AB
P.O. Box 1305
171 25 Solna   Tel. (08) 705.97.50
                         Téléfax : (08) 27.00.71

SWITZERLAND – SUISSE
Maditec S.A. (Books and Periodicals - Livres
et périodiques)
Chemin des Palettes 4
Case postale 266
1020 Renens   Tel. (021) 635.08.65
                         Telefax: (021) 635.07.80

Librairie Payot S.A.
4, place Pépinet
CP 3212
1002 Lausanne   Tel. (021) 341.33.48
                         Telefax: (021) 341.33.45

Librairie Unilivres
6, rue de Candolle
1205 Genève   Tel. (022) 320.26.23
                         Telefax: (022) 329.73.18

Subscription Agency/Agence d'abonnements :
Dynapresse Marketing S.A.
38 avenue Vibert
1227 Carouge   Tel.: (022) 308.07.89
                         Telefax : (022) 308.07.99

See also – Voir aussi :
OECD Publications and Information Centre
August-Bebel-Allee 6
D-53175 Bonn 2 (Germany)   Tel. (0228) 959.120
                         Telefax: (0228) 959.12.17

TAIWAN – FORMOSE
Good Faith Worldwide Int'l. Co. Ltd.
9th Floor, No. 118, Sec. 2
Chung Hsiao E. Road
Taipei   Tel. (02) 391.7396/391.7397
                         Telefax: (02) 394.9176

THAILAND – THAÏLANDE
Suksit Siam Co. Ltd.
113, 115 Fuang Nakhon Rd.
Opp. Wat Rajbopith
Bangkok 10200   Tel. (662) 225.9531/2
                         Telefax: (662) 222.5188

TURKEY – TURQUIE
Kültür Yayinlari Is-Türk Ltd. Sti.
Atatürk Bulvari No. 191/Kat 13
Kavaklidere/Ankara   Tel. 428.11.40 Ext. 2458
Dolmabahce Cad. No. 29
Besiktas/Istanbul   Tel. 260.71.88
                         Telex: 43482B

UNITED KINGDOM – ROYAUME-UNI
HMSO
Gen. enquiries   Tel. (071) 873 0011
Postal orders only:
P.O. Box 276, London SW8 5DT
Personal Callers HMSO Bookshop
49 High Holborn, London WC1V 6HB
                         Telefax: (071) 873 8200
Branches at: Belfast, Birmingham, Bristol, Edin-
burgh, Manchester

UNITED STATES – ÉTATS-UNIS
OECD Publications and Information Centre
2001 L Street N.W., Suite 700
Washington, D.C. 20036-4910 Tel. (202) 785.6323
                         Telefax: (202) 785.0350

VENEZUELA
Libreria del Este
Avda F. Miranda 52, Aptdo. 60337
Edificio Galipán
Caracas 106   Tel. 951.1705/951.2307/951.1297
                         Telegram: Libreste Caracas

Subscription to OECD periodicals may also be
placed through main subscription agencies.

Les abonnements aux publications périodiques de
l'OCDE peuvent être souscrits auprès des
principales agences d'abonnement.

Orders and inquiries from countries where Distributors have not yet been appointed should be sent to:
OECD Publications Service, 2 rue André-Pascal,
75775 Paris Cedex 16, France.

Les commandes provenant de pays où l'OCDE n'a
pas encore désigné de distributeur devraient être
adressées à : OCDE, Service des Publications,
2, rue André-Pascal, 75775 Paris Cedex 16, France.

3-1994